PASTURES NEW

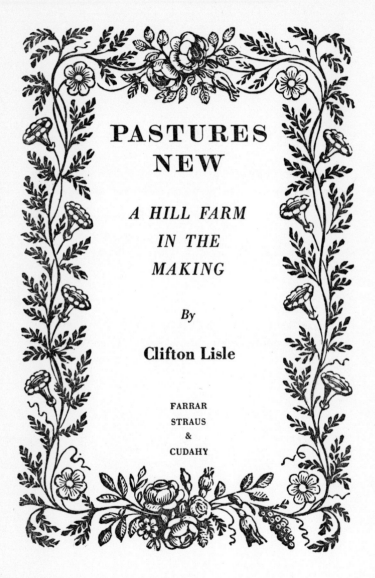

PASTURES NEW

A HILL FARM IN THE MAKING

By

Clifton Lisle

FARRAR
STRAUS
&
CUDAHY

To

A . H . L .

Without whose encouragement and patience

Our work at Melbrook

Would have proved barren indeed

Contents

PASTURES NEW

"Ille terrarum mihi praeter omnes angulus ridet."

"When the desire cometh, it is the tree of life."

1

THE SEARCH

THIRTY YEARS are a long time, peace and war, to call a place one's home, but they pass like the shadow of a summer cloud when the making of a garden has lain at the heart of them, filling each moment with delight.

To tear up roots so deeply nourished, to leave a well-loved spot so rich in memory where so much has been given through the years; nay, so much more received in happiness—this has a pang all its own, a special and particular pang for the priceless gifts that a garden brings.

Yet there must be no indecision about it, no heartbreak of half and half. It is stay for good or go for good. And the sooner decided the better. Perhaps there is an instinct back of it. The sort of thing that sets the tern and the plover stirring when their time to move has come. In any case, my wife and I within a week knew that our days close to the city were ending. The strange thing was that there seemed nothing to debate. A day came and we understood without comment that the next step for us must be a farm, the smallest of all possible farms, yet clear of suburbia.

Life being what it is, complications were not slack in arriving, but our decision was instant, wholly irrevocable and rich with the exciting lift that comes with sureness of intent. The great thing is to know one's mind. As with most of us, the first complication was of the earth earthy. What in the world would we buy a farm with? Our answer to that one was the response that always seems so easy and so natural until tried. Sell the old place; buy the new. It was as simple as that. Just how we expected to coordinate such a deal troubled us not at all—at this stage.

So the cottage and its garden and its fruit and its flowers were listed with hopeful agents. That pang over, the first real thrill began and surely a thrill it is to set one's mind in earnest on a quest. There can be no repining once that starts. It's far too exciting. It has the tang of the morning about it, of feeling young again. Besides, finances and settlements and the paying of bills are too far off, too shadowy and too vague at the moment, to bother with.

Big places, small places, incredibly charming places, old places, some not so old, impossible places, were we to admit the truth, all came merrily as grist to our mill. Obviously we had limitations to guide us which asserted themselves once we had passed the first fine careless rapture of seeing what we could not possibly buy nor afford to live in were they ours.

Our farm must be small, very small indeed, for we hoped to handle it largely ourselves. We knew roughly how far away it should be from our former home. That led us to a consideration we had not thought of. What of the length of lanes and driveways? Half a mile of meandering road can be joyful enough in summer, but in winter who will clear the snow or dig us out? How near is the nearest road regularly ploughed by state or township? Though we had not considered it before, the solution of that lies in the ubiquitous school bus. Wherever schools have been consolidated in the country, busses go and where the busses go, there go the snow ploughs before them—a boon to all.

FOR SIX MONTHS we devoted most weekends to the search. How lovely, even in dead of winter, deep country can be! How alluring, how appalling, some houses are. In fairness, most of those we saw were alluring. One in particular warmed our hearts the instant we saw it. It had everything. A shady lane, pine bordered, a glimpse of the house angled at the end of it, spruce and pine above to break the wind, leftward the old stone barn, its woodwork fresh with paint. Then, prize of it all, the glint of water under winter sun where below the house a stream had been dammed to form a pond of size.

The house itself was something to dream of. Small, very old indeed, built solidly of stone, boasting two fireplaces in one room, surely not an act of supererogation on the part of the colonial builder. We knew the place could not be matched and we knew as surely the price would prove beyond us. It did. The search went on.

For variety, we saw and knew in an instant farms that would not do: here was a place, and good it was to look upon, fresh tortured by the cut of a highway cruelly slashed across it. The price was helpful; the four-lane road was not. A woodland cottage came next, far too along a lane where snow would certainly drift and ice lie long. A hillside farm, and right enough it was, at a price we might reach, but— and a big "but," too—just visible at the top of the hill a telltale hint of a ranch-type, picture window, lamp and all, to warn us what that hill would crop before too long. We were wary now.

A spate of mansard roofs had their turn, most excellent for good garrets, a sturdy, sensible type they are, but scarcely beautiful. We knew how cool their high-ceiled rooms would be in summer. How costly to heat in winter.

Then, in sharpest contrast, two smaller houses. One a perfect gem of weathered field stone and handwrought ancient beams, not a picturesque head-bumper among them, yet the beams were there all right where they had been for centuries. The huge fireplace was unspoiled, a joy to see. And round about on every side, even now in March, were signs of a love for gardening that made the place unique. Miles of rolling, unspoilt valley to the south were not the least of its charms. It was the cream of those we had seen, but this time a lack of land deterred us. We were not looking for much, but one field did not seem quite enough.

Again and again we came back to look at it, well into spring, when the whole place was a mass of daffodils and primrose clumps and the glory of lilacs and roses to come. Hard it would be to find a spot more enchanting. Centuries had gone to its making. Foot by foot we went over it with our friend, that master craftsman, Reuben Nock, who had built much for us at home, watching as he probed the aged joists and rafters and window jambs with his knife for soundness or climbed to study the shingles from the garret below. The place was irresistible. In mind's eye we spotted our furniture here and there about its rooms and hung our pictures on the walls. We even estimated the cost of a tiny library for our books. The house was all but sold and we the buyers—till in the end we decided no.

All this while, of course, our old place had not been sold. We were coming to appreciate the difficulty of selling and buying simultaneously. If we bought first, how could we pay the purchase price? If we sold first, where would we live?

What of storage that mounts up? One thing was sure before
very long. We had to sell when we bought or before that,
storage or no. There could be no easy purchase, no easy
move, for us, with leisured sale advantageously to follow.
Offers for the old place came nibbling in; some good, some
bad, some so-so, but not good enough. So on we went with
our hunt for the farm.

The second of the smaller houses, and it was another gem,
also lacked land, but it was bewitching to explore the
brick-floored, ancient kitchen on the ground level, now used
as a sort of den. Here were the same hand-wrought rafters,
the same field stone, as in the other houses. Possibilities
were endless. But again a lack of land stood in the way.

Since then, we have seen both of these houses often. Good
friends of ours live in them now. No other places in our
search—except the very first—approach them in beauty of
setting or in loveliness of planting, so mellowed through the
years. How love for a place does tell.

ONE DAY, in very early spring, driving with our agent
through the hills, we turned into a lane by way of short-
cut, passing without a glance a farm on our right.

"That's for sale, too." Our friend casually nodded. "But
it wouldn't do."

By then we were near the barn, the Swiss bank-barn
commonly found here, its red front showing a white horse
and two six-petalled tulips for luck. We craned our necks
to see what would not do and why.

"Too much land for one thing. You say you want it
small. And too much price, I'm afraid."

True enough on both counts, but there seemed no harm
in looking. Once inside that farmhouse door, we knew we
had come to our journey's end. It was as simple as that.
And just as surprising. Naturally, the details of sale and

purchase soon stirred to vex us, and uncommonly vexing they proved as such things can be, but as with our decision to move in the first place, so now, once we knew our minds were set, we were content.

By June we had bought the little farm, the place we had all but passed without a look. And by some quirk of fortune, in June we had sold our old place. Fate had been kind indeed.

Stone house, small, four windows across the front, stone barn, oak-beamed, oak-pegged, not a nail to its framing. Large springhouse by the walnut trees, some thirty-six acres of land, a hillside pasture, coppice above, a field to the east, yielding rapidly where junipers encroached, a field uphill to the west, already a wood in the making—walnut, poplar and maple fighting it out for survival with mats upon mats of honeysuckle—oddly the saplings winning, say, twenty-four acres of arable land, most of it slope, much of it sadly starved and eroded—the place was ours, plus what was worth as much again and more, the surprise of wild strawberries ripening in the sun.

Now a wild strawberry patch in June hereabouts is not of necessity surprising but these were—or their forebears. Not until the place was almost ours, bought and paid for, did we recognize just what we had taken seisin of. High on the slope above the house, just where the hill levels off, on either side of a footpath where a hundred years ago there ran the old Nantmeal road—Nantmoel, the Glen in the Wild, as the Welsh called it—there grew our strawberries. And there, too many years ago to reckon, I used to climb that selfsame slope each June to taste the first ripe berries, wild and sweet. Not that we lived nearby, but a good twenty miles across the Valley, a long way to ride or walk before motors had cut distance.

It seemed incredible. All unknowing, coming to the farm by car, hill and berries naturally far from mind, I gave no

thought to those days of long ago until I found that hill
our home! There must have been fate back of that, a kindly
fate one does not always find. I would have bought the
place almost for the strawberries, so bravely they carried
one through the years and the wars to long ago.

The house was small and solid, in no way picturesque,
but built foursquare of honest field stone. Unfortunately the
rough-hewn rafters and beams we had found so welcome in
the two smaller houses had been ceiled over. Our house also
lacked its original fireplace, the wide-mouthed, authentic
kitchen hearth, typical of farmsteads in this neighbourhood.
For a while we thought it might have been plastered over,
as many were when Franklin stoves came into fashion, cast
at Hopewell and nearer Warwick. In our house, however,
the great fireplace had gone for good, worse luck, in some
former alterations.

Speaking of old houses, we find it refreshing to hear
people of our countryside refer by particular names to the
stones used in dwelling and barn and springhouse. Our
friend, the mason from the Corner, as he was repointing the
barn wall at Melbrook after we had lived here for a while,
called attention to this by showing us what really had gone
to the old walls' making—flintstone, granite, niggerhead,
orangestone, pepper-and-salt stone—he named them one by
one and rated each at its proper worth.

Field stone had sounded so simple to us. Actually, its
beauty is as varied and as lovely in texture as a tapestry.
It was not long before we began to look at walls a bit and
marvel at them, for we realized what we had missed by
taking them for granted.

Again our friend the builder with his genial son-in-law
Ed, and Art to help him, made a careful tour, stabbing and
probing with his knife to see what was sound and what was
not. Luckily nearly everything proved firm. Before we had
really decided what could be done to the house at once, what

we could afford at the moment, and what must wait its turn on the budget, another coincidence cropped up to match the strawberries, if not to pass them.

When we bought the farm, weeks before work had started on the house, I had written the postmaster at our nearby village, two miles away at that, asking him to have my mail left in the former owner's box at the turn in the lane. This was done. When work began and the carpenters were busy, it seemed an opportune chance to drop down and thank the postmaster whom I did not know.

It was then that the real miracle began. There seems no other word for it. Being given my mail through the grille, I was casually asked if I had ever been this way before.

"You mean before we bought here? Yes—a long time ago."

"How long would that be?"

"Too long to reckon. Why?"

"You wouldn't have been riding a horse, would you?"

"Come to think of it, I was. Why?"

"You wouldn't have gone to a farm to get him watered, would you?"

Had I been asked these questions in any other way, my mind would have drawn blank. I am sure of that. Now suddenly memory snapped vividly to life through forty years and more. Details of a boyhood ride, forgotten for a lifetime, were forming, growing clearer. I took up the story myself in a kind of dream, seeing each incident in its proper sequence. That was the mnemonic, I suppose.

"Yes, I did ride up here once. I asked at a farm if I could water the horse. His name was Dick. He was a bay. I remember that. I'd come twenty miles already and almost as many more to go. I got the water all right and a feed of oats as well. And then a dinner for myself so good that I could tell you what they gave me—even now. I think I really could."

"You wouldn't remember their name, would you?"

"It was"—again the miracle—"it was Vail."

"My name is Vail," said my friend, as unperturbed as ever. "I was a boy in that kitchen when you rode up the lane. We all had dinner together. I've remembered your name."

Memories were crowding now. "There was an old man there. He sat with me on the porch after dinner at noon. Your grandfather?"

"Yes. You wouldn't remember his name, would you?"

"He told me. Wait a minute. He told me he was very old. He said he could remember bonfires on the hills in England, where he'd been born. They were to celebrate the passing of the Reform Bill in 1832. His name was—wait a minute. It was Longland. Benjamin Longland!"

I could not have thought of that name very often, not consciously, since the day we had talked there together on the porch. How vivid it all was. I even recalled his asking me if I had ever read Samuel Butler's *Hudibras*—something assuredly I had not. I could hear again the man's chuckle in his beard as he recited for my astonished ears:

> *Compound the sins they are inclined to*
> *By damning those they have no mind to—*
> *And prove their doctrine authordox*
> *With apostolic blows and knocks!*

What an amazing old man he must have been!

In the end I left the post office knowing I had found a friend. But how can such things be? To buy a farm and find one's youth again—in wild strawberries on a hill? To post a letter and see the years roll back for almost half a century? I learned that day how long country memories can be. And a day or two later I had proof of country kindness.

As I was gouging out a five-foot tangle of weeds masking
an old asparagus bed I had not known even existed, a man
I had never seen before came down the lane on a tractor.
He had his cutter-bar attached and asked if I had thought
of cutting the weedy west field. Naturally I said I must get it
cut some day, when I had time to find someone to do it.
In an hour that field was neatly shorn—and all for nothing.
When I tried to make it a business matter and pay for it,
as I certainly should, my friend just shook his head.

"Got to welcome a neighbour, mustn't I? I knew your
brother well over at the Grove."

I'd had no hint of that.

Not three days later another kindly soul across the road
surprised me with the gift of three or four tons of sheep
manure, to nurse the old asparagus back to life. His reason
was the same. A welcome to his neighbour. I had never
seen him before.

Such things are startling these days. They certainly touch
the heart and give new meaning to life, changing our picture of human nature.

We never knew so many friendly folk could be so kind,
especially to strangers. Or were we strangers? After the
strawberries and the postmaster, I began to feel like the
oldest inhabitant come home to the hills. Surpassing kindness from our neighbours has not ceased. Lilac shoots and
flower slips to start our garden with from Pippin Hill. A
kitten, too, to teach our moles their manners. Two boxwood
bushes and a great basket of daffodil bulbs from another
friend by Pigeon Run. Seeds, lima beans they were, for our
first vegetable patch from a friend who helped us plant it.
Week by week all through that first summer, and ever since,
people made us know we had come home. One day our
house was filled with flowers, a surprise from Bryncoed in
the Birchrun hills.

WHAT A SUMMER it was! Everything had to be done, so it seemed, at once, and well before anything else. Some sort of order, however, was hit upon and a table of priorities set up, though not always followed. How dull life would be if it were. First came the house. Naturally we wanted to move in. Before that could be, we tore the inside of it apart and put it together again with surprisingly little change.

The very first task on the place, even before Ed and Art had driven the first wrecking bar into a partition, was the felling of three large and dying apple trees along the lane. They were too far gone to save. For good measure, two or three sycamores came down also. Big ones. How horrible it is to drop a living tree, yet these had to go. The result has proved worth the crime for now a view has been opened from the front of the house down across a pleasant water meadow, masked before, where sheep are grazing, and on across the curve of the brook and the millrace to where the wheel of an old mill shows through the trees.

The cutting of the sycamores reminded us that the world has a practical side we must heed. It is not all a dream of youthful rides and ripening berries. An estimate was given, down came the trees, ripped through like saplings by a power saw. Devastation lay on every side. How huge can a felled tree be? We soon knew and we knew a bit of human nature, when the cutter, resting from his well-paid labour, casually asked if now we'd like an estimate for lopping off the branches and cutting up the logs. He was within his rights, of course. His estimate, as he pointed out, had been · for felling trees. That lesson sank deep. We lopped and cut and split and moved that mass of timber ourselves, a young friend from college helping, as we stored the firewood in the barn and burned immense piles of brush and branches when they had dried. Since then, we are more heedful of estimates. Actually, our friend was trying us out.

He found us fools, but left us wiser. Since then he has done excellent work here—always at a reasonable price. Perhaps he too learned something when he found us tackling ourselves the appalling work of clearing up. One thing we did gain from it—enough good firewood, well dried now, to last for years. And we burn a lot of it on our hungry hearths. Of all the trees that grow, apple wood is the sweetest in fragrance, bringing memories of spring as the old logs burn of a winter's night. Ash and sycamore kindle well, even though green.

THE HOUSE, as we have said, we found a simple three-story building of well-pointed field stone, with a small, one-story ell to the rear, also of stone, containing kitchen and garage. Downstairs there were but two rooms apart from the ell, both comfortably large, a sitting room or parlour into which one entered, and adjoining it, both of them making up the front of the house, quite a large dining room. From this one reached the kitchen to the rear. From the dining room, stairs led to the second story, easy stairs, pleasantly turned halfway up. Someone had taken pains in the old days with that stairway, alternating two simple designs of turned work in the banister uprights. The windows in the dining room are obviously askew in the wall. No careful architect reared this house a century ago, but the men who did built surely and well. Its very irregularities are a delight.

Upstairs were four very small bedrooms and a bath. Still above, were four other very small rooms. Our plan for remodelling was simplicity itself—to save expense it had to be. Downstairs, ground floor, no structural change at all, until we could build the little library. Second floor, knock out partitions and so form two large bedrooms out of four small ones. In doing so, we left space for really large closets in each room, a good four feet deep and plenty wide. Old houses, one soon discovers, had no closets. Wardrobes once took their place.

Space was found in making over our two larger rooms to turn a narrow passageway between them into a linen closet at one end and a fair-sized toilet and enclosed shower at the other, thus providing two bathrooms and ample closet space on the second floor. The main part of the second-floor hall remained as it was at the top of the stairs.

The third floor we treated in much the same fashion. Partitions came down in a shower of plaster and laths. Across the front of the house on either side of the third-floor passage, new partitions were built forming two very large closets, each with windows. These are really small rooms, holding an immense amount of storage. Few things we have found more needful.

Space was left on this floor for a large room on the west side of the hall, a bathroom, and a smaller bedroom on the other. What more could we need?

Wiring and plumbing sound more complicated than they were. Two partitions out on each floor and others built in for closets and a new division of space, this, in addition to the bathrooms, was the actual change. As always happens, of course, more had to be done than expected. For one thing, some of the old flooring had to be replaced. The wiring proved a nightmare of threads and patches held together by tire tape. Generations of former occupants must have had a hand at mending and extending it. We tore it out ruthlessly for safety and rewired. New copper pipes and new bathroom fixtures went in throughout—something that shook our budget to the core, but we were determined to get the fabric sound inside and out, whatever happened, and not have to rip things apart again later.

One discovery made early on was that we could not easily unceil the hand-adzed beams as we had hoped. They had been partially cut here and there for pipes and wires, and completely unnecessarily. How stupidly people ruin things most worthy of preserving. Some day we may see what can be done with these old beams. Certainly they are worth trying to save if possible.

In the living room downstairs we had two problems. One —how to provide a cloak closet—was solved readily. We built a closet or cupboard-like affair of wood, with top and side shelves for good measure, out from the wall between the windows and the door, thus recessing them both by some three feet. Unpainted, the effect was not pleasing at all, but once the closet and its door had been painted the same cream white as the walls, it retreated to proper scale— in fact, it improved the appearance of both door and windows. Incidentally, the four windows of this room fill it with light and sun. Also, they keep it fresh and cool in summer wherever the breeze.

Our second problem, not quite so easily solved, was the fireplace between the two east windows. Remember we had no architect in all this. We were working things out as best we could ourselves, probably very much in the way the house had been built. The actual opening of the hearth was wide enough, but the total spread of the chimney jambs seemed contracted. Incidentally, the chimney extended about a foot and a half into the room. A single board by way of mantel accentuated its narrowness. In the end, we gave up looking for a really old framing. Prices were exorbitant. Many pieces were no longer sound, especially at the base where the old wood had rotted. So we searched catalogues for reproductions of good mantels, finding a lovely simple one whose original is in the American Wing of the Metropolitan Museum, its age corresponding roughly to that of our house.

The opening of the reproduction fitted our fireplace perfectly with just an inch to spare on each side. That was a bit of luck. The spread of the new mantel shelf and framing extended, so we found, ten and a half inches on either side of the old chimney, thus allowing us to make good use of the space between the facing and the wall. We built in here a shelved cupboard at either end as high as the mantelpiece, not opening to the front, of course, where the new facing was, but to right and left of the fireplace itself.

The whole room was changed for the better by this. The fireplace and mantel, like the cloak closet, had taken on a pleasing scale in proportion to the size of the room and the size of the hearth. The two narrow cupboards are invaluable. Above the mantel we left the narrower chimney as it was.

While at it, we relaid and extended the bricks in front of the fireplace, just to play safe. With old pinewood floors, dried for so many years, it does not pay to take chances. One good spark or live cinder in a crack and the damage can be done. Usually it is.

Speaking of fires, we did a lot of thinking about the roof. It was of shingles, well weathered. Our friends, pundits in such matters, embarrassed us by commenting on it and expressing relief that it was of honest wood, as they called it, not composition material. We swallowed our pride, however, and a sense of the esthetic, if we have any, by considering the consequences of open hearths burning wood all winter, the possibility of sparks on the roof and what a fire in the country means, once it has started. So we had another go at the catalogues, seeking shingles this time. Some fire-resistant ones we found were good enough in colour and texture, which is just as important, not to be eyesores. We miss the weathered moss of the old roof, of course, but feel the safer. Better still, the new shingles, whatever they may be made of, are beginning to weather a bit themselves. Perhaps we were wise.

The dining room needed no change except a different

spacing of wire outlets and plug-ins. In the kitchen we saved
the cabinets, but put in a new stove, sink, dishwasher and
other labour-savers.

While all this was going on inside, my wife and I made
plans for our only real addition, the small one-story library
wing, extending west from the dining room. A door already
there conveniently saved us the cost of knocking one in the
wall. The room as it finally appeared was 28 feet long by
15 feet wide inside, with a really large fireplace at the far
end.

We built the library walls of stone to match the old house.
Luckily, an old dry-stone wall once bordered the abandoned road, the Indian road running towards Yellow
Springs and Nantmeal that now climbs the hill behind the
house. Here and there great blocks of the wall had fallen.
A mason who not only knew stone but loved it went over
that wall rod by rod, selecting the sizes and the colours he
needed. It would be hard to tell now which part of the
house has stood for a century and which is new, so cleverly
did the master mason lay up his walls and match the
pointing.

My wife, mindful of her winter flowers, drew up the plan
for a large bay window facing the sun south-by-west. There
was to be a door, the upper half of it glass, in the middle of
the bay window, opening on what we hoped would be a terrace. Inside the bay, on either side of the door, are deep
shelves for flowers. Copper trays have been made to fit
them, removable in summer. Underneath are bookshelves.

The walls of the library, apart from the fireplace and the
bay, are also faced with built-in shelves, some 4 feet 10
inches high. To get a sizable air space above the ceiling,
we allowed the walls above the bookshelves to go straight
up some three feet more to the eaves, then sloped the ceiling inward for three feet more on either side, following the
slope of the roof above. At this point, however, we used six

great rafters, straight across, their under halves exposed from the plaster, thus ceiling off the angled space above them, for some six feet below the ridge of the roof. In short, the outside of our little wing has a normally pitched roof. Inside, however, the ceiling is almost coved, if there be such a thing as a cove with the curve taken out of it. I wonder what an architect would make of our work. In any case we like it. The result is satisfying, the dark beams contrasting well with the white of the plaster between them.

The fireplace was difficult. Three times our patient friend the mason began it, only to be told it was too narrow, or too shallow, or too low. Besides, we wanted the actual hearth raised by two bricks' height above the floor of the room, and this to be done in two stages; the outer edge of the hearth one brick higher than the floor, the firebed another brick higher than that.

The floor of the library also was to be of brick. This was chancy. Would they sweat as bricks can? How chilly would they be in winter? To play it safe, there being no need for a cellar here, we dug down for three feet and filled with crushed stone. Then a layer of cement, two layers of the thickest tar paper, a second layer of cement and we were ready for the flooring of bricks, nicely shaped large ones from Maryland. Oiled and waxed, they are coming into their own rapidly. Better still, they are warm in winter under rugs as they are cool in summer without them.

These alterations took time. Building the library took even longer for it was not until late in fall that work even began on it. Enough had been done to the original house, however, for us to move in by mid-August. Wisely we had remade the top floor first, plumbing and all, then the second and finally what little had to be done downstairs. By so doing, painters were not held up, for they followed the carpenters and electricians downwards floor by floor.

While still living in our old house, we had carried load

after load of packed china and whatever could be squeezed in a car up to the barn of the new place. In the end, I suppose several moving-van loads were transported in this way a little at a time at no cost. Peach baskets may not have been designed to carry wineglasses and china, but it speaks well for my good wife's packing that not one piece out of hundreds was cracked or broken.

WELL BEFORE WE MOVED IN plans had been made for some sort of garden some day. In fact, two of them, one for at least a few flowers and one for as many vegetables as we could manage. The latter was important in our little farm's economy. Obviously the midsummer move and all the rest made a vegetable garden out of the question the first year, but once we had settled in, though engulfed by a madhouse of carpenters and plumbers and painters, we still found the time to decide where the vegetable garden should go, how large we should make it and what could be done the first fall, only a month or so ahead by now, by way of ploughing, manuring and mulching for winter.

Our plans for future flowers were based primarily on economy of effort. With the rest of the farm on our hands, the vegetables to boot, we wisely decided to limit our flowers to three beds near the terrace-to-be, with, perhaps, a border inside the terrace itself where a dry-stone wall lacked planting. Or would, when we had built the wall. What a dream world we lived in! How wise our resolutions! How soon broken!

Two years have passed, but our three little beds have crept up, unnoticed, to another bed of old-fashioned roses—who could resist their scent in June?—to climbing roses at the gate, more roses by the barn door, a triple row of bank roses along the drive, climbing roses on three sides of the house, clematis, trumpet creeper, silver-lace vines, myrtle bed, where do such things end? Why is it so impossible to resist them?

There were to be two shrubs, great Chinese hollies moved from the old place. These and what were already growing here must suffice. Yet now, by our second summer, we have planted more than threescore others, not to mention twenty-six fruit trees, but of them anon.

The very first year, even before we had moved in, we made our first planting. It was a row of dahlias near the weed-smothered asparagus bed. When the first bud opened late that August, we knew we had taken root. Gardening had begun again and flowers at that, in spite of all our good resolutions. The dahlias had come to us a kindly gift from Rough Acres near home.

On the place, as were bound to be about an old house, we found waiting for us a generous growth of flowers and shrubs, the old-fashioned sort. Hollyhocks, tiger lilies, plantain lilies, lemon lilies, blue flag, peonies, summer phlox, rambler roses, lilac clumps, sweetshrub, rose-of-Sharon, flowering quince and almond, a spicebush near the kitchen window, some lovely dogwoods. We did not know until our first spring here, a year later, how many daffodils there were, grape-hyacinths, daylilies and the like.

ONE OF THE GREATEST SURPRISES that spring was an immense climbing rose, or clump of roses, across the brook, where blossoms reached twenty feet and more up into the trees and hung in fragrant festoons over the water. How the roses got there no one now remembers, but they are obviously very old. We seem to be the only ones to share their scent and beauty, though actually they are not on our land.

WHILE THE WRECKING and rebuilding were going
forward indoors and a general clearing up and burning outdoors, long debate was held about the verandah that ran
across the front of the house. To be or not to be? Like the
melancholy Dane we could not make up our minds. How
strange to decide in a few minutes on selling an old and
comfortable home to venture upon the uncertainties of a
run-down farm in the hills, then to shuttle back and forth
undecided, unable to say whether a porch should stay or go.

Under its roof was a pleasant stone-flagged retreat, most
inviting in summer sun, most comfortable in summer showers. Finally sun and shade decided for us. We'd risk the
showers. Once the new terrace had been built where we
planned it, in the southwest angle formed by the library
wing and the old house, we knew that it would bask in
afternoon sun but be shaded and cool in the morning. The
verandah, on the other hand, if turned into a terrace, would
reverse this, being sunny in the morning and shaded later.
So down came the porch roof—which needed repairing at
that. The increase of light indoors, especially in winter, was
astonishing.

For shelter by the front door, which is at the northeast
corner of the house, we built a small new porch extending
the depth of the stone-flagged terrace and about the same
extent in width. It has, of course, proved useful summer
and winter, being wide enough to cover a long wooden
bench.

And so the first summer raced by, our half of it, piles of
trash from the builders seemingly gaining in spite of all we
could do to burn and bury and cart away. Some fourteen
tons of it, old and new, were removed. Yet always the thrill
of something new was there to spur us on. For instance, as
the library walls went up, we could begin staking out the
little terrace and finding just how many bricks we should
need to pave it, old bricks from some torn-up sidewalk.

Until then we had no idea how hard it would be to find them. Nor did we know that, like Aladdin's lamp, old bricks, weathered in sand, never cemented, colouring through the years under the sun and rain, are more costly than new ones. Luckily, there was no rush, for the library work dragged interminably.

When the old bricks did come, we laid them on a crushed stone and sand foundation, leaving space on all four sides of the terrace for a narrow flower border, edged with tilted brick. To make the terrace level, we had to dig a bit into a slight slope uphill to the southwest away from the house. This gave an ideal excuse for a low dry-stone wall or ha-ha, retaining the bank and walling in the terrace some two feet above the border. The top of the ha-ha naturally was level with the grass slope on that side.

Since then the wall itself has been planted with some of the simpler wall-flowers—stonecrop from the lovely cottage of Arley up the lane, a bit of ivy here and there, a winter jasmine at the corner—in two summers the trick was done, thanks to earth between the stones and a natural moisture working through. The wall of the terrace seems as old as the house now, a comfortable, at-your-ease sort of look about it, provocative of tea when the day's chores are over.

DURING OUR FIRST SUMMER, however, nothing was planted except the dahlias. By fall a good many bulbs had been put in, but none close to the house, where everything was still dismally a-clutter with sand and stone and cruel piles of cement. It was not until the following spring that we got to work in earnest on the little terrace borders and the ha-ha. It was then that we started the wall flowers. It was then that the plan of the old house, the new terrace and the simplest of nearby beds began to shape.

As the length of our drive had depended on the proximity

of a snow plough, so the extent of our new beds and borders was limited strictly by the stretch of a garden hose, the closer in the better. The farm from the very start made inroads on our time undreamed of. That was inevitable. We were wise, we were very sure of ourselves, until we bought several more lengths of hose and stretched our good intentions considerably.

And so our first summer sped towards fall—nerve-racking, disorganized, infuriating past all bearing with delays, yet unbelievably happy. Actually it took us well into winter to see the last of the builders, but they were busied with the library only. The house itself was fresh as paint and comfortable. Delays, however, gave us time to look ahead and plan a bit. The vegetable garden, the flowers and the fields lay far ahead, of course, each with its particular challenge. All that must wait. We could get the fall bulbs in. We could dream of blossom ahead. Whatever the future, our hearts were in the trim.

"He that tilleth his land shall have plenty of bread."

2

SETTLING IN

OF COURSE, not even our first half summer and fall
were devoted entirely to reconstruction, digging ourselves
out of debris and planting a small row of dahlias. On all
sides fresh chores pressed in that had little to do with the
house and its mending. For one thing, although we had
moved in, the new kitchen gear had not done so, and we
still had to eat. The inn at the Eagle in Uwchlan took care
of that, although our host must have been surprised to hear
my wife and me knocking hungrily for breakfast well before
seven. Our busy days were all too short. By suppertime, we
were back at the Eagle again more famished than ever. So
good was the fare at this 155-year-old inn that we have
dropped in for dinner there almost once a week ever since,
not at all surprised to find many of our friends doing the
same.

Fair weather or foul, grass grows. That presented another
challenge. We thought we had it licked when we arranged
with a lad from a neighbouring farm to mow for us. As a
starter, Noel and I set out to buy a power mower. If ever
since gasoline engines were invented, anything could prove
more cantankerous than that particular mower, we have
yet to be plagued with it. It ran flawlessly whenever the
repair man heeded our pleas and came to see what was the
matter. Once its mender had turned his back, it choked,
shook despairingly and stopped dead, obviously determined, like the old man's clock, never to go again. Grass
cutting our first summer was a nightmare, but a long
drought and early frost put an end to that. The grass with-
ereth, the flower fadeth, we are told. And they did.

Between whiles we tried our luck at pruning our one
bearing apple tree, a Yellow Transparent, sawing off dead
limbs which were saved for firewood or, if rotted, dragged
by our neighbour Philip's jeep to a pile for the burning.
We had bought the place from him. Whenever in doubt, we
run to him for aid. He's never failed us yet. What is more,
no one in the world could be more kind than his wife who
cheers our hearts at unexpected moments with the gift of an
oatmeal loaf, warm and fragrant from the oven. What can
be more delectable than that? Harriet's has a flavour all its
own, made the richer by her kindness.

WE WANTED the vegetable garden next spring to be
on a gentle slope above the barn, between it and the house,
because here in the old days there had been a chicken run.
We knew how enriched the soil must have grown through
the years. Some of the ground along the edge of the garden
site had reverted to sycamore and walnut saplings and a
tangle of blackberry bushes woven overhead. Clearing
them proved beyond our powers alone, so Bill from college

and Frank soon to graduate from school, both of them
giants, pitched in to help, Noel lending a hand with his
tractor and chains until by mid-September we had yanked
out scores of young trees by the roots. A cutter-bar, a disk-
plough, then a tooth-harrow, several times repeated, completed the transformation.

The tractor came into play again as we tore up yard
after yard of broken wire netting along the boundary of the
abandoned chicken run. Much of it had been buried a foot
in the ground. They had built that run wisely against
marauding tooth and claw.

Two walnut trees of size, one at each end of the run,
came down next. Finally, as the ruined henhouse yielded
to Bill's wrecking bar, a swarm of hornets did not. What
a Donnybrook that was! A spray gun finally brought them
to heel, not without wounds on our part.

ON DAYS when our helpers could not come, attention
was turned again to salvaging the old asparagus bed. Hundreds of pounds of matted sod, roots six inches deep, had
to be pried loose by hand without breaking the stalks of
the asparagus that by some miracle still grew from them.
A crawling, backbreaking job at best. The bed, once cleared,
with weeds and sod carted off in a barrow, received heroic
treatment—kill or cure. Two hundred pounds of rock salt,
every whit, went on first to finish off any surface weeds
we might have missed. This is, of course, normally done
in spring. Then one hundred pounds of pulverized cow
manure were scattered over it. Finally, and surely few beds
of asparagus have been so dressed before, a three-inch
mulch was applied of the old pinewood sawdust scraped
from our floors when they were being resurfaced. It worked
like a charm. Not a weed showed all summer.

Much later, in November of that year, two tons of fine,

well-rotted sheep manure, a gift from our neighbour at the mill, was disked into the bed. Then a hundred pounds of bonemeal, to spark it. Also we added lime, always needed by asparagus. That neglected bed has come on famously. By our second summer we had more asparagus from it than we could eat and quantities to freeze for the winter. Weeds were controlled our first spring by more salt, then, cutting over, by a mulch of salt hay. This has been repeated this spring. In mulching, care must be taken to avoid what is called thatching. This is the use of any material that tends to mat and so form a rainproof roof, the very reverse of that for which we mulch in the first place. With all its care, the old bed seems to have owed most to the sawdust. That really did give the weeds their *coup de grâce*.

By the time we had the worst of the saplings out and the garden space in order, other woes cropped up we had not expected. There were heavy clumps of hydrangeas everywhere, far too many and obviously spreading. By the end of August we knew they were not much for bloom, so out they came, all of them. We found it surprisingly hard to grub up their roots, but every rootlet we overlooked in the ground sprang into vigorous life a week later, enlivened no doubt by its pruning. We grubbed. They grew. *L'appetit vient en mangeant!*

A clump of old-fashioned pampas grass, nice in itself, seemed too eager to take over the lawn, so out it came. For good measure, we hacked out some excessive forsythia and moved a growth of Indian currants, the coralberry. These we saved for their clustered berries in the fall. One juniper, a big one, had to be sacrificed. It stood right in the middle of our view across the water mead and the brook. What can be harder than destroying a tree? Or more lovely than a wind-rippled pool, sheep grazing beside it? The tree came down—and up. Frank was standing belt deep in the pit before we had the last of it out of the ground.

OUR STRANGEST BIT of tree-felling, however, was that of a sick poplar standing within a foot of the kitchen wall. We had to drop it carefully away from the roof of the kitchen below. Also we had to prevent its striking two good buttonwoods in its fall. There could be no mistake in this job, for we did not want a smashed roof whatever happened. Our budget was suffering enough as it was. Frank swung the axe, but could let it bite at the tree on one side only, the wall of the house being too near on the other. This is not orthodox felling with so thick a tree.

Suddenly someone thought of the long climbing rope, a nylon, used on Mount Washington the winter before. Somehow we got it looped well up on the tree, again thanks to Frank's agility as a climber; then, as he axed away at the butt, Eugene and I tugged, ready to drop rope and run as the trunk toppled over. Run we did! And the poplar toppled, steered by the rope fairly between the buttonwoods.

How strange to think that less than a year before I had been caught on that selfsame rope, falling from the ice wall above Tuckerman's. It had come in handy then, that rope, just as it had now guiding the tree fall.

So content did we feel with our luck that we knocked off work a day or two later and walked for miles on the Hopewell hills, eating our fill of wild grapes on the way. Can anything be sweeter? It seems important to avoid being hounded by a garden. Or for that matter by a farm or anything else. How easy it is to let even non-essentials back up and master one, turning joy into misery. My wife and I have tried to avoid that, not always with success.

A fortnight after we had moved in, however, swamped to despair by all that must be done, we wisely stopped doing anything at all one lovely afternoon and went to see a small horse show nearby. It was just the bracer we needed. All classes were for working hunters, most of them ridden by our farming neighbours in shirt sleeves. It was a warm day. There was nothing fancy about this show, but plenty of good riding. The jumping by children, and there were many, was superb. An hour or so of that tonic put home chores in their places. They no longer choked and goaded us. It did not take us long after that to understand how necessary it must be that we have little breaks like this from time to time.

BACK AT THE FARM, we spruced up the barn and the old springhouse with a good coat of whitewash inside and out. What a difference that made. Every day the cutting and hacking, the clipping and clearing and raking and piling went on until it seemed impossible so much brush could be gathered. Heaped high overhead, it was burned each week, yet still the great piles grew and their fires glowed deep in the night. There seemed no end.

"Th'essay so hard, so sharp the conquering!"

One joy came to us that first Labor Day, a long, soft rain to revel in, as it broke our drought. Can anything bring more heartsease than rain to parching fields? Or more cheer to withered flowers? Or to our own hearts, for that matter? It is good to know that, drought or not, the Lord still opens unto us His good treasure, the heaven to give the rain unto our land in His season and to bless all the work of our hand.

A LITTLE BEFORE this our household had been augmented by the arrival of Alena and Eugene, two not so
young D.P.'s from the Ukraine. Kindly and willing they
were, though bent above all on converting us to their ways.
That they might yield a trifle to ours never occurred to
them. They did, however, during the year they were here,
provide us with a liberal education in unsuspected ways.
Their food, for one thing. For anything we ate, they had
a stock reply.

"Ah, Missus, eet iss not goot! We not eat thees in
Ukraine."

And they'd have none of it. When asked what they did
want, they said, "Eet iss groats, Missus. Und svine. Und
borsch. Und sugar. Vot else?"

What in the world groats might be, my wife had no idea.
Nor had I. Nor had any of the grocers we knew. In the end
we found some, nine miles away—coarse cracked wheat,
actually. Eugene seemed to thrive mainly on bacon and
sugar. Seven pounds of both a week were a trifle to him.
Poor souls, I suppose they had been starved of sweets for
years.

To see Eugene with a scythe was to watch a master and
no mistake. Slowly, smoothly, he would cut his swathe,
without seeming effort, yet leaving the sod like a lawn
behind him. He never bent over or reached. His sweep
was unhurried, sufficient but no more, back saving arms
and arms saving back, all in easy sway and rhythm. Always so many paces and then time out to sharpen the
blade.

No one in this neighbourhood had seen the like for generations. Passing farmers, as good as they come, stopped
to gaze at that old man scything, fascinated by his ease
and pace.

To find him a scythe that suited was another matter. The
blade must be Austrian, of course. The snead must be of

ash and straight. There must be a tiny block of steel by way of an anvil for sharpening. A hammer of steel, the best, to go with it. Of the hardest steel.

"These vill not do. Eet iss too soft!"

Scythe, blade and all, was easy, but the anvil stumped us. We drew eight towns in the county blank on that. Yet somehow Eugene managed to tap his blade to a razor's edge and keep it so. He rarely honed it.

The day he found a scythe to his taste was one of terror to me, for he stood in the middle of a small country store, swinging the blade this way and that testing its spring and the hiss it made in the air, regardless of anyone's neck, till he had the floor to himself, with leeway to spare.

We learned a lesson that day, too, for no sooner had he decided on the blade he wanted than he got to work adjusting the doles or handles on the shaft. Heel of blade to lower dole, just the distance from the ground to his own hipbone. Distance between lower and upper dole, the distance from his fingertips to elbow. All new to me. Yet this, of course, lay at the heart of the matter, magic skill with minimum of effort. Before Eugene left the hardware shop, he had an audience caught by the spell of it. We were getting back to fundamentals.

Being in a buying mood, he added to his purchases a wheelbarrow, an axe, a hammer, a small emory wheel, and several small files—although he liked none of the latter.

Nails were another abomination to him. Eugene could mend or build anything, provided we kept him well stoked with bacon and groats and sugar.

"Barn-house, eet need—you see—"

He had little English, but I saw all right as he showed where a sheepfold should go, where a stall cried to be set right again or where three great uprights must be restored to their places under the old threshing floor.

All this took nails, but no nails in all America were right.

"Nein! Nein! Eet iss too dick! Too dick! Ach, eet iss too beeg! Eet iss too small! Eet iss no goot!"

In the end, bad nails or no, the work produced was matchless. Always the craft, the skill of hand and eye were there, a joy to see.

Alena had more English, but not much. Smiling delightedly, she'd say, "Yes, yes, Missus" to everything whether she had understood a word of it or not. Confusion reigned and all of us were happy. Between them they shared a small dictionary. One day, walking up the lane to Melbrook wood on the top of the hill, they viewed a great buck with proper head of horn. Excitement was intense as they rushed down hill to tell us. "Eet iss a—eet iss der grosse—" Alena ran for the dictonary. Eugene thundered on, arms stretched wide to show us. "Eet iss a—ach—" The dictionary had arrived. "Eet iss a stack! Eet iss a' art!" It could be neither, but it was a white-tailed buck all right.

A few weeks later, frenzied barking of Garry, our springer, and great cries from Eugene brought me on the run towards the barn. The old man was wild.

"Eet iss a—eet iss a stack! Garry at stack in barn-house! You see! A gun you haf'?"

By now, I was as excited as Eugene. His arms were waving. How Garry could possibly have brought a deer to bay, especially in the barn, in broad daylight, I did not know. By the time I arrived I found he had not. It was a groundhog back of some boards. Eugene had taken the word stag to mean any wild animal, not of necessity a deer. Excitement had done the rest. Never a dull moment! I shot the woodchuck, maybe saving a little corn. Maybe not.

IT IS A SPORTING COUNTRY here and no mistake. We have game and to spare with plenty of hunting—fox, deer, rabbits, pheasants are everywhere. Our first fall in-

cluded time off for a hound show at the Rose Tree, the
opening meet of the Treweryn beagles, a pony show at
Canby-Lodge and the Radnor Races. With the Treweryns
at dawn we hunted two and a half brace of hare. It was, I
hate to admit, my forty-fourth year at it.

How imperceptibly, how surely, the seasons merge. Midsummer, then our move here in August, and now a few
weeks later going over the high ground near Orrelby for
the evening paper at Miss Mattie's in the village, I could
sense the coming fall. It was still quite hot. Few, if any,
leaves had turned. Yet the feel, the scent of autumn were
here none the less. Goldenrod by the wayside, wood asters,
jewelweed, the touch-me-not, wild sunflowers, chicory, and
the sharp, clear beauty of the sky at sunset, almost an
autumn sky; how rich life can flow. We knew well by now
what was meant by the hills being joyful together.

IT MUST HAVE BEEN along this very lane that part
of Washington's army trudged after Brandywine and the
near thing at White Horse in 1777, when rain suddenly
ended chance of battle before a dozen shots had been
fired. The Continentals lacked bayonets. Priming wet, they
had no choice but withdrawal. Lord Howe had marched
unopposed down the Swedesford towards Schuylkill. Washington and his ragged troops had crossed the Great Valley,
finding it boggy that day, climbed Bacton Hill, then down
over Pigeon Run past what is now Rapp's Corner, to Pine
Creek and the valley of the Pickering and so to the Yellow
Springs. As early as 1750 the Springs were popular for
their waters. That phase has long since passed. Here the
army camped to lick its wounds from Brandywine. The
buildings there were augmented by a large new building
of wood, erected at Washington's order, and the whole
little hamlet turned into a military hospital. It served as

such during the heart-rending winter that followed at Valley
Forge.

How easy it is for us to forget such things living in this
peaceful countryside today. Yet there is scarcely a church
among the many old ones hereabouts that was not used as
a hospital to supplement the larger one at Yellow Springs.
Somewhere inside these churchyard walls one can often
find a simple stone. They are alike in what they tell us.
Sacred to the memory of twenty-two Revolutionary soldiers
buried here— Near this stone lie twelve unknown Revolutionary soldiers who died of wounds in this church—
None of these men were famous, but all were faithful. Many
who died of wounds or typhus or smallpox were buried at
Uwchlan Friends Meetinghouse as well as near the East
Vincent and the East Pikeland churches and by some of
the country schools. The old Welsh name of Uwchlan was
originally Ywchlan, meaning the place above the valley.
It is well called, lying high among its lovely hills.

Some of these soldiers' graves, near farmlands, in what
was then sparsely settled country, have long since been
forgotten and ploughed over. Others are still marked; a few
walled in. How easily we forget all this. Or the fearful
havoc wrought in our quiet meadows by war. It is of record
that one farm alone lost 10,000 rails plundered from its
fences for campfires. Split one rail and see the labour it
takes. Years must have gone into erecting the high snake
fences that surrounded the fields in those days. The passage
of the armies, even without battle, destroyed them in a
night.

THE ROAD to Yellow Springs, now called Chester
Springs, followed by a part of Washington's army, is now
the overgrown lane that comes down our hill, fades to a
narrow stretch of greensward a rod or so west of our new

terrace, passes the old asparagus bed to its right, the road
trace still perfectly clear, then comes to life again in the
part of the Indian road still used across Pine Creek.

The Horseshoe Trail, a godsend to those of us who long
to walk in peace and quiet, follows this old lane for a
while and the graveled road beyond it.

As we sat on the lawn one day that first autumn
here, our chores for the moment well in hand—actually it
was 175 years to the day since Washington's march past
here to Yellow Springs, although we did not know this at
the time—unexpected friends chanced by and stopped to
share a cup of tea and a bite of homemade cake. First on
the lane, riding a comfortable old grey, was our lovely
neighbour from Skycastle up the valley. The grey shared
some cake with his mistress and seemed to like it. Then
came Bill from college. Then Philip, our helpful neighbour
from the east. Five lads with heavy packs came next. Such
things, in the midst of hard work, delight us, weaving the
happy pattern of our life here. Unfortunately, we cannot
offer pick-me-ups of tea and cake to all who ride and trudge
the trail. As a matter of fact, to save embarrassment on
our part and theirs, we have moved the footway across the
field at no inconvenience to its users. A rod off the terrace
was a bit too close, especially after a troop of cavalry came
trotting by one day. How surprised they would be to know
they were in the tracks of the Continentals. Recently a
neighbour found two Revolutionary cannon balls by his
house near the Trail, obviously dropped from an ammuni-
tion cart on the march from Brandywine.

The 26th of September, Argonne Battle Day, is a red-
letter day here, for on it Garry came to us, a two months'
old springer puppy. It is needless to say who has ruled the
house ever since, broken all proper regulations, galloped,

ears whirling, through flower beds, outvied mountain goats
in leaping where he should not leap, especially on clean
clothes, and made of himself an unremitting, bedevilling
nuisance, secure in the knowledge that we wear him in our
hearts' core. What a larrikin he is!

THE 2ND OF OCTOBER that autumn we began work
on what we hope in time will grow into a little orchard
though negligible now. At this stage we could not expect
to plant regular trees and live to enjoy much of their fruit.
All very well to console ourselves with classic tags—*sero
arbores quae alteri saeculo prosient*—but dwarf trees, early
bearing, seemed wiser at our age, at least a mixture of
dwarf and regulars.

The sloping meadow west of the house was well disked
first. Later on, in November, we set out 22 different trees.
They included: apples, 4 McIntosh, 2 Red Delicious, 2
Golden Delicious, 2 Courtlands, 1 Baldwin, I Winesap and
1 Clapp Favorite; pears, 2 Seckel, 1 Bartlett; cherries, 2
Tartarian; peaches, 1 Elberta, 1 Golden Jubilee, 1 Hale
Haven and another unmarked.

In planting this little orchard, we took considerable
pains, digging the tree pits far deeper than needed for their
roots. The pits were then partially filled with good soil
and cow manure, mixed half and half, and then filled up
with water. When the water had sunk in, the trees were
put in place, more good soil but no manure tamped down
around them. Each tree was then staked and given a mulch
of straw and manure, with more water. Last of all the
young trees were safeguarded from rabbits and field mice,
so we hoped, by close-meshed wire screening three feet
high. We sank the lower edge of this wire well into the
ground to discourage mice who are always attracted to the
winter cover of mulch. As time went on no trouble was

noticed from mice, but deer caused some damage last winter to the tender branches, as deer will.

Our second year we put in four more trees—two apples and two cherries—in front of the barn. This, for their blossoms as much as anything else. Baldwin and Smoke-house for apples. Black Tartarian and Napoleon for the cherries.

F ROST CAME EARLY—dahlias had blackened by the 3rd of October. On the thirteenth of the month, the first wedge of wild geese honked overhead, low flying, as they crossed our valley southward. Yet the pasture by the mill-race was as green as ever, sheep, slow grazing, reflected in the waters of the brook. Colour we saw a-plenty. Soon every glen and glade of the Pickering flamed with it—crimson and russet and gold. We knew then, as we had always known, how lucky we had been to pitch tent here at Mel-brook.

How fruitful this countryside really is. Having lunch one Sunday at a neighbouring farm, we found almost every thing on the table home-grown except such things as coffee, sugar, salt and flour. The latter could have been. Milk, cream, butter, eggs, three or four vegetables, fruit, herbs for the salad dressing, most delectable mutton, mint sauce, these honest fields had yielded all, showing how far skillful farming can go.

Frost and rain, Indian summer, more gentle rain, slowly the library wing went up, desperately we did what we could to save the nearby lawn from ruin as the last of the bulbs went in. Glory-of-the-snow, patches of snow crocus here and there and snowdrops—once they called them February Fair Maids or Candlemas bells, for their early blooming. And snowflakes, the old-time Loddon lilies, these clustered beside the great rock where climbing roses grow. Our first planting included also daylilies, phlox, some peonies, hyacinths, tulips, jonquils, campernelles, winter aconite and blue squills. Clumps of daffodils were scattered outside the old barnyard wall and near the springhouse. We have seeded many gentians by the spring, but so far had no luck with them.

It was mid-November when the kitten from Pippin Hill brought in his first mouse. That started him hunting in earnest till soon a mouse or a mole a day seemed part of his ration, with a bird or so for dessert, we fear, but wisely he kept such tidbits hidden. Garry did his best to vie with him, but in vain. We celebrated the kitten's first kill with a flagon of cider sent us by a friend from Devonshire. It was as good as champagne and spoke with authority.

ABOUT THIS TIME the roof of the addition was shingled so in the place of honour we put the old weathercock from Tyrol that had adorned the lychgate of our former garden. We also put up the other weathervane, the little Tyrolean man with his rake and scythe and his burgermeister pipe. He went on the pent that roofs the farm bell. How deeply memory warms to things like these. They do more for us in other ways, bridging transition from war to peace, just as they bridge our move from old home to new.

Although, as has been said, little could be done the first fall and winter beyond planting bulbs and clearing up, we did look ahead far enough to install a coldframe, too late unfortunately for that autumn's planting. There just was no time for it. While at it, we built the best sort we knew, digging down over 4½ feet and removing all soil. The pit without its walls measured close to 7 feet each way. The lining walls were of cinder block, the usual thickness. They cleared the surface of the ground by an inch or two. On the bottom of the pit, lined with close-meshed wire, we scattered sizable stones to facilitate drainage. The pit was then filled up with a mixture of cow manure and the best topsoil we could get and some sand, well watered as the layers went in. Actually, manure, soil and sand were thoroughly mixed, not laid in layers, but we felt it important to give each foot a thorough soaking as the pit was filled.

The work took a lot of time, but we hope that coldframe will serve us a long time. Later, a second frame of the same size was made, so that one could be used for early garden seeds and the other for seeding early flowers. Each coldframe is completed by the usual wooden sides, above-ground, perhaps a foot high, sloping towards the foot. Each is covered by two 3 by 6 glazed tops, thus making them easy of tending. They are used now all winter.

TO TAKE OUR MINDS OFF the crawling pace of the library, the weeks when nothing whatever happened as one man waited for another to fetch what a third had for-gotten—none of this caused by our good friend the builder —we broke our already straitened budget into bits by putting in a post-and-rail fence along the lane. It warmed our hearts to see it, but had each rail of each panel been of beaten gold, it could not have cost us more. That fence was cruel extravagance, there is no denying, but what a morale builder it was, too. No foxhunter can glimpse a post-and-rail without a lift of the spirit and a yearning for more of it.

ONE OF THE EARLY first fruits of the farm, coming to us gratis, was a harvest of shellbark nuts falling just where the old lane ends. It took a lot of trouble to shell

them and pry out the meat, but the cake my wife made
was a prize. Next time, however, she says she'll gather the
nuts, thank you, and let me ready them for the baking.

WHEN WE CAME to the farm, we found several of
the fields here had been planted on shares, most of the
small profit, if any, to go to the man who had worked
them. Too often under this method land is starved merci-
lessly. Corn, usually the money crop, goes in year after
year, regardless of impoverished soil. Fertilizer is stinted,
little or no manure or organic matter of any sort going on.
This was the case here. Some corn was harvested on the
upper fields. Some soybeans were combined on the west
fields, but poor, sick stuff they were. The robbed and
hungry soil under the stubble was pathetic. All we could
do as a starter was put on lime and plenty of it.

These worn-out fields presented a problem, our greatest.
To get all of them into shape, even were that possible,
would be beyond our means. What we could do, however,
was stop more robbing of the ground, lime generously
everywhere, then next spring hope to get at least a field or
so into grass with a cover crop perhaps of oats, thus preventing erosion and making a start at some return.

All this lay far ahead in our dreams that fall, but we
did see more clearly the plan we should try to follow. Now,
two summers gone, we have all the land except for an acre
or so well on its way towards grass, using both oats and
wheat as cover crops. A little at a time has shown results.

We are glad naturally to see honest sod coming in. Weeds
must go, but even at that we miss the glory of the wildflowers now confined to the verges of the wood and two
slopes we have decided to leave to the trees. Incidentally,
we are setting out white pine and spruce on these slopes,
seedlings sent us by the State Forestry people. But the wild-

flowers—how cheering are the blue cardinal blossoms below the spring, dayflowers under the old stone wall, white
wood asters brightening the coppice, blue asters and the
goldenrod, boneset and Joe-pie. Some day we must list the
wildflowers here, spring to fall. There is no lack and all
are lovely. After all, are not our strawberries wild on the
hill? Were they not wild and as tasty when all the world
was young and gay?

ALTHOUGH MANY TREES have come down, for
good reason we hope, some have gone in, apart from the
fruit trees. Among them, planted early on, a swamp maple
near the turn of the lane for the fire of its leaves in fall.
A Kousa dogwood near the terrace for its blossoms when
other dogwoods have passed. A Washington thorn and a
silver-bell, the last for its scent as well as its beauty. A
redbud for old times' sake.

Speaking of trees, how surprising the wychhazel can
be each year, come upon unexpectedly blooming long after
winter is with us. Some of them in Mine Hill wood, up
Noel's way, our first November here, reminded us of the
wychhazel that grew under the hackberry near the home
we had left.

As CHRISTMAS and the New Year approached, I
went one day to see a neighbour about manure. Naturally
he needed all he had for his own fields and had none to
spare. As we stood on the hillside talking, suddenly he held
up his hand.

"Hark to em! It's Orville! It's the hounds!"

Wes, my friend, climbed by the seat of his tractor to
listen. I had not heard a hint of hounds in cry. He had.
For years to follow them had been his heart's delighting.

I could hear them now myself, very faint, far down the valley somewhere near Woods Edge. They were chiming well together, not much scent, not much pace, but plenty of old-fashioned music as they owned the line. As always in these old packs, one or two hounds called the tune, their bell notes sheerest magic.

Wes was as taut as they were.

"We'll view! That's Orville's horn! As sure—look!"

There, not fifty yards away, a great dog fox, white-tagged, his coat as red as red, glided out of the wood and stopped to watch us.

"Tally-ho!"

It was foolish to view, for all we did was head that wise fox back, but who can be wise at such a moment, faced by the thrill of a good fox breaking? The fox, however, knew his own mind and where he wanted to go, halloo or no. A moment later he broke covert again a few yards further down, then glided as smooth as a drift of smoke across the winter wheat below us towards Melbrook. For half a mile we watched him go.

Orville, his daughter Bertha whipping in, galloped up, cheering hounds as they recovered the line we had all but lost for them. He was as eager as Wes. What hunting lore shone in that keen old face! He has been cheering hounds now for more than sixty years, still sharp to go, lithe and tough as a whalebone whip, showing his field the way. His daughter can turn hounds to the horn and follow them hard all day as few men can.

The desire accomplished is sweet to the soul. We could hear him harking merrily as he galloped downhill.

"Orville's happy today," said Wes wistfully. I agreed. Both of us knew what we were missing.

What a country it is to hunt as well as to farm in our hills. How rich the land in water, for one thing. This is reflected in the names of the homesteads, most of them

built before the Revolution, a few in the 1600's. Spring
Mill, Spring Dale, Spring Lea, Spring Hollow, Spring Lane,
Springhead, Pebble Spring, Sycamore Spring, Spring
Meadows, Pickeringbrook, Willowbrook, Tipton Brook, all
of them sing of water's blessing. Each old house was built
by a spring, of course, or even above one, as is the case
with our own. Even in these years of killing drought, the
deep springs flow sweet and sharply cold from their limestone sources in the hills. People are prone to forget the
cycle of drought we seem to be in. They little note its im-
port. The first six months of 1954, for instance, showed less
rainfall than ever recorded for such a period since the
establishment of the weather bureau. The over-all rainfall
of the past twenty to thirty years has been steadily decreas-
ing, water levels falling. Here we are thankful for our
streams, and grateful to Him who sendeth the springs into
the valleys which run among the hills, who causeth the
grass to grow for the cattle and herbs for the service of
man.

IT SEEMED NO TIME at all for our first half year
to pass, so busy we were, so much still to be done, yet
always we looked for the spring. That is natural on the land.
Christmas came before we knew it—on Thursday, reminding us of the old saw.

> *If Christmas on a Thursday be,*
> *A windy winter you shall see,*
> *Windy days in every week,*
> *Wintry weather strong and thick,*
> *Summer shall be good and dry,*
> *Corn and beast shall multiply.*

The adage proved true. For a tree this Christmas, we had
a small four foot balsam on a table. Garry's curiosity was

still too keen to risk one he could reach. Swags of ever-greens at door and windows were also out of reach. My wife made the whole house gay with these.

By way of wassailing our little orchard, we gave each tree a dash of Devonshire cider, with an extra dash for the old Yellow Transparent.

> *Health to the good old apple tree!*
> *May you bear hats full,*
> *Caps full, three bushel bags full!*

It would seem we'll wait quite a while for all that.

SNOW REACHED us at New Year's to Garry's de-light, until he had gulped down too much of it and nearly died. That was a scare. The Pickering hounds chivied a fox along the hillside beyond the lane. We trudged through the untouched snow towards dusk to greet our friends at Arley cottage, sky clear, gloriously so, sharp blue overhead, then near evening jade green above the Uwchlan hills. What can transform a country lane as snow does? What sound can stir memory so surely as the scrape and clack of skates on a country pond?

When the first snow had gone, we found a chance to widen the narrow drive that led by the east end of the house to the kitchen ell. Its width was fair enough for a jeep, but too tight altogether for much else, especially with snow and ice to contend with. This work called for a bull-dozer, as 4 feet of steep bank had to be cut away for a distance of 10 or 15 yards. Before that, a dry-stone retain-ing wall had to come down, only to go up again when the bulldozer had completed its work. While at it, the ground near the new terrace was graded a bit, an easier job.

Towards the end of January, we shared in an extra-ordinary feast at the Eagle in Uwchlan, when the innkeeper there invited everybody in the countryside far and wide to a venison dinner as his guest. We went there with Jamie and his family from Pigeon Run. It sounds incredible but over five hundred people shared in the feast that wintry night. And good it was! Serving began at five o'clock in the afternoon and kept up, so they say, till nearly midnight.

On the farm odd jobs never ceased. Gabriel Junks, our lead peacock, was lugged from the barn to his new strutting place on the terrace wall. Two little horseshoes from Iceland were nailed on the barn door for luck. The sundial from High Ongar and further back from Spring Bank was fetched to where we hoped our flowers would be. These by way of amenities. On the practical side, tons of rock and subsoil from the bank had to be carried away. Someone has noted that country life is not quite the garden-pathery and lushness beloved by its portrayers who usually live in the city.

Coming again to embellishments, St. Francis and St. Fiacre, from the old place, were removed from their peach-basket packings in the barn and restored to their rights. St. Francis under his little pent on the side of the walnut tree where there are plenty of birds about him in summer, as we found out later. St. Fiacre, to the side of the library window indoors, but overlooking the herb bed and the terrace borders. We felt really at home seeing both of them in place.

On the 7th of February, a pail of ashes carefully saved from our old hearth was spread on our new one and the first fire lighted in the library. Twenty-two great boxes of books were soon unpacked, resorted and shelved. A hard task but a happy one. How friendly old books are. And how they can be missed.

Things moved even faster after that. Signs of spring were everywhere. Soon daffodil tips were inching into view, always the first thrill. By Washington's Birthday, bluebirds were with us and Canada geese, northbound, had explored the creek. Gorgeous they are, like swans. Black of head and neck, a showy throat-piece for good measure. How short a time it seemed since they had arrowed by us southward.

WILD DEER WERE ALL ABOUT and sweet to the heart it is to see them, troublesome or not. One day well on towards the season's end, hounds met at Springhead, then drew the coverts above Spring Lane for fox. They found there nicely but too well, for seven deer broke covert, the fox among them. Cannobie Lee had nothing on us. There was racing and chasing for fair that day, all the way down to Diamond Rock, for it is illegal to hunt deer with hounds and the pack had to be headed and stopped at all costs. Yet to see those seven deer silhouetted against the sky above Felicity as they pointed for Nyala and Pebble Spring was a picture no one could begrudge. Later that day, hounds now safely on fox gave us a glorious view as the rascal slipped from the Mine Wood. Our old friend Caspar, who follows faithfully by car, spied him first and made the hilltop ring as he shrieked his Tally-ho! Caspar can make himself heard when needed.

All this was February, and that means spring. Seeds for the vegetable garden had long since been ordered and were waiting. Four trenches had been dug for a new asparagus bed beside our garden to be. Little we knew how useful the old bed would prove down by the lane.

On the 25th snowdrops appeared, first blossoms of our first spring here. Garden and truck patch and fields had spoken.

"He hath made everything beautiful in His time."

3

FIRST SPRING

SPRING IS A MIRACLE in spite of the hackneyed phrase of saying so. Even those who see nothing of it respond to the magic of rising sap, to the stir of life in the world's old bones. Only, of course, there is nothing old about spring or the world either when that miracle occurs. Each meadow and glade is fresh-spun as on creation's morning. All can share with wonder in the glory, yet how few bother even to look. Fewer still to understand.

First hint is a stir among the birds. Our winter familiars, the nuthatches and tufted titmice, the woodpeckers and the chickadees, are more talkative all of a sudden, as they busy themselves at swinging feed tray and suet bar, usually upside down. We note this. The cardinal, whistling and chatty all winter, has taken on new notes, the same, yet different. Bluebirds, were they with us all winter? Suddenly there are flocks of them. And then, surest token of all, the flash of a redwing above the withered, brittle cattails where the stream has shallowed, widening to a swampy patch.

That sets us going in earnest. It must be now or never for the odds and ends. Once let real spring reach us and there'll be no time for any of them. As a starter, peat moss was scattered on the euonymus with which we were trying to heal the wounds of the bulldozed bank. Trenches dug for our new asparagus bed were 18 inches deep. Thanks to our good friend Horace, who comes to help us in a pinch, these trenches were ready well before the new plants came. One ton of cow manure and 100 pounds of 5-10-10 were worked into the soil ahead of time. Few things indeed can do much growing without nitrogen, phosphates and potash, in one proportion or another.

HORACE LIVES a good way off, over by the river. When he does come to us, however, he comes early, usually hard at work by six o'clock. Often he has lent a hand at milking his neighbour's cows before that. Like Eugene, he never hurries, but a day's work with him is honest measure. He can wear down many a younger man by noon.

THE FIRST OF MARCH brought meadowlarks, not much for song just yet but cheerily talking things over, home hunting, like most young couples. It seemed time to get our garden tools in order if we hoped ever to do it, so one day we cleaned up the workshop in the barn and arranged places to hang the spades and rakes and hoes, the scythes and axes, the forks and brush hooks, all the paraphernalia that go with a garden as well as the tools one needs on a farm. Heavier gear was kept elsewhere. Strange to think that the word paraphernalia once meant a bride's dowry. As my wife works over her vegetables, I wonder if she knows this. I'd better not tell her.

Eugene taught us many things, among others how to save energy by keeping tools edged for the work at hand. He whetstoned even shovels and spades and hoes until one had to handle them with care or lose a toe. What a job they did in use though. His axe was a razor.

Poor Alena and Eugene. We miss them. How hard we tried to tempt them with our vegetables fresh picked, the tenderest of corn or lima beans, all that the garden brought us in season. It was no use.

"Eet iss our tooth, Missus. Ve cannot eat eet."

And back they went to beets and groats. Surely groats are tougher than new green peas. *Chacun à son goût.*

We loved them, but how stubborn they were. After all, this was a hill farm in Chester County not the Ukrainian plain. Take the matter of stones. I explained to Eugene one day that the garden must be raked before we could seed it. Frost had brought stones to the surface, some large. All were easily seen. Eugene shook his head.

"No ston'. Nock! Nock! In Ukraine no ston'! In garden, no ston'!"

They were there all right, hundreds of them, before his very eyes. I pointed them out.

"You not understan'! In Ukraine, no ston'. No garden haf' ston'. Thees garden no ston'."

A strange *non sequitur* if ever was one.

It seemed hopeless, for there the stones were. He could not witch them away by denying their presence. What went on in his mind as we raked them clear I cannot fathom. It had nothing to do with the labour involved, for he had not a lazy bone in his body. But he held to his point all year. Whenever stones were mentioned, he'd say:

"Ah nock! There iss no ston'."

In the end, I won a partial victory by tossing stray stones

from the garden to the grass beside it as I worked a row. Inevitably Eugene's scythe would strike one and quick he was to call me to account.

"Mein Gott! Nein! Nein! Eet iss ston' you put eet there! You mus' not do thees!"

When Eugene got a bit too set in his ways, Alena in her kerchief would shake her head.

"*Conservatif!*"

When she thought that my wife and I were a bit fussy ourselves, she'd put us in our place with a sly, "*Pedants!*"

One real victory nature won. My wife had warned both Alena and Eugene of poison ivy, showing them the shiny green of the three-leaved vine. I did the same.

"Nein, Missus, Nein! Nock! Nock! In Ukraine, thees poison no!"

"It's poison here all right! You'll see. Just don't touch it."

The old man smiled at our ignorance, then bent deliberately and plucked a cluster by the roots. He paid for that all right. For the next week he was tortured, face, arms and legs swollen with poison and discoloured with the concoctions we gave to relieve him. Alena even rubbed him with touch-me-not leaves, a remedy suggested by my wife. From then on he had no argument on that score. It was the only time we saw him yield to American facts of life. Whenever I got the sprayer out and lugged it about squirting poison ivy where I found it, Eugene would drop what he was doing and run to join me.

"Keel eet! Ve keel eet! Mein Gott!"

EARLY MARCH GAVE US the first crocus. Philip and Harriet with Peggy and David and Stephen came to see us, bringing as a present a beautifully wrought wren house. Our initials had been burned into the front. No one we know can do such marvels with wood as Philip Jenney. Far and wide he is known for his skill in restoring furniture, especially the priceless museum pieces still to be found in some of the houses here.

Just as a kickback, we had snow the next day, but birds were everywhere so we belled the cat. This may have done some good in the beginning, but it soon defeated its purpose by making a special brand of stalking so necessary that no wing was safe. We really had taught the cat its job.

ST. ANDREW'S PEEPERS, the hylas, shrilled in the marsh by the 13th. Thoreau speaks understandingly of them.

—there leaked into my open ear the faint peep of a hyla from some far pool. One little hyla, somewhere in the fens, aroused by the genial season, crawls up the bank or a bush, squats on a dry leaf, and essays a note or two which scarcely rends the air, does no violence to the zephyr, but yet leaks through all obstacles and far over the downs to the ear of the listening naturalist, as it were the first faint cry of the new-born year, notwithstanding the notes of the birds. Where so long I have heard only the prattling and moaning of the wind, what means this tenser, far-piercing sound? All nature rejoices with one joy. If the hyla has revived again, why may not I?

IT REVIVED US enough to remark the Horseshoe Trail with wooden arrows, painted yellow, where we had switched the footpath across the lower meadow to the wood. While at it, Frank and I trimmed some dead branches from two walnut trees. Eugene uncovered the old asparagus bed and raked winter leaves from the flower border beside it. Two hundred pounds of rock salt went on the asparagus.

My wife seeded her first tomatoes in flats. Pritchard Certi-
fied, they were.

By mid-March, bloodroots were everywhere. Indians
used their stain as a dye. Spring-beauty had whitened the
banks of the lane and liverwort was peeping through leaf
mould in the wood. How warm its leaves and stem are kept
by their fuzz. Cheered by the sight of them, we planted 10
Valentine and 2 Chipman's Canada Red rhubarb at the foot
of the garden. We sprayed the fruit trees for scale at this
time, glad to see that all had survived their first winter.
Sycamores and the evergreens, spruce, white pine, juniper
and arborvitae, were also sprayed. We had found at the
old place how well it paid.

Two sweetshrub bushes and one abelia, old-fashioned,
always favourites with us, were dug up from where they
were being smothered by trees. We replanted them near
the vegetable garden, but had ill luck there for all three
died that summer. Probably we forgot to water them properly when the drought was on. It is interesting to note
how each success is checked by failure somewhere along
the line, keeping one into the collar, as it were.

MY WIFE, needing no such urge, tried the new roto-
plough on the garden the moment the soil felt right for it.
The wretched thing, but her heart's delight, promptly ran
away with her as she clung to the handles. Now and then,
for variety, it would plunge backwards when intended to
go forward. Every movement, front or rear, was executed
with sudden, unpredictable jerks and lurches. This was in
the beginning. Now she has tamed the vicious thing, handling it almost as nonchalantly as the ladies who stroll up
and down their garden rows in advertisements. I must
admit that first ploughing was rugged. The ground, in spite
of our disk-ploughing in the fall, was thick with wiry

bramble roots and clumps where stars-of-Bethlehem had matted. Twice and three times my wife went over it before she had got it into tilth to suit her.

Daffodils and forsythia came to us together on the 22nd of March to cheer us in all this toil. Soon after we put 300 pounds of lime on the lawn. It needed it. Then, unmindful of our resolutions that there would be no planting here except in the truck patch, we saw the month out by putting in a small spreading juniper by the bank steps, a pussy-willow further up, a Washington thorn by the corner of the terrace and two cherry laurel by the wall there. Two cedars—junipers, they really are—were dug up on our hillside and put in by the library wing. We had to get help for that. A border of blue periwinkle was planted beside the drive, lily-of-the-valley pips among it. That was another mistake. The lilies-of-the-valley began to take over in no time, so we pulled them out, preferring the green of the myrtle all year, in addition to its lovely flowers.

Twenty-six small English ivy plants were put in by the new chimney end and along the ha-ha wall as well as above the retaining wall where the bank had been cut back. My wife keeps us well supplied with ivy, growing snips of it in water, then rooting them in sand and loam until ready for transplanting.

WHEN WE CAME to the farm here, we found two ilex—Japanese hollies—on either side of the porch steps. These were given a deep mulch of rotted leaves this spring, with a trowel of aluminum sulphate under it, worked into the soil 6 inches out from their stocks. We also gave the Kousa dogwood some for luck. It didn't help it. Hollies, leucothoë, azalea, cherry laurel, mountain laurel, all respond to this, as soil acidity is essential to them.

Our set-out flowers were few the first year, so much else

had to be done. A handful of primroses, some English daisies, some heartsease and pansies, mostly yellow, a few mixed, some violas, these were about all we found a chance to put in the terrace borders at first. By now, the winter aconite, planted last fall, was in flower. Even this year's jasmine had blossomed. Daffodils were everywhere in not too skimpy clusters. We knew everything could not be done at once. It would be no fun if it could. We'd plant as time and the budget allowed.

Tulips, unfortunately, had fallen a prey to mice or moles. Scarcely any came up. That was our third failure, just to keep us steady on the traces. Mole traps do no good. We hesitated to use poison on Garry's account, although he seems able to gulp anything and survive it. Once he swallowed one of my wife's earrings and once he scrunched up the remains of an electric-light bulb. No harm apparent.

APRIL BEGAN with a final cleanup. Final, for the moment. We're still at it. How incredible is the variety of discards one finds about an old place. I reached once to yank a rusty chain from the ground. It took a lot of yank; more than I had bargained for, but in the end a spike tooth harrow came up. Another time, I got to work on a bit of innocent-looking wire and uncovered a bedspring. No monotony in our farming.

TO HELP US this April Fool's Day, Jamie came over and Philip brought his jeep. What we do owe to him and to that useful car. We filled it high with logs from a sawed-up telephone pole and then we used it to lug off stones raked from the garden. Jamie also helped knock out some partitions in the barn to set the sheep pen right—

the sheep-pen-to-be, that is. We burned giant pyres of brush, saving apple prunings for sticks in our pea rows.

Meanwhile, we were disk-ploughing the west field. That afternoon the Soil Conservation Agent came over to stake out contours on the slopes above the barn. Noel ploughed the key furrows later that day. It is encouraging to see how the contours and strip farming have taken hold in these hills. Erosion is cut each year.

Few of us realize what grass can do on a slope. At a farm across the Valley, a friend of ours put most of his land in grass for grazing steers. Within a few years several new springs, or rather old springs dry for a generation, began to flow again following their original traces. Surely this is one proof of what happens to water levels, with and without grass.

The first week in April showed *Scilla sibirica* and hyacinths out. The moles or mice had spared most of these. Our new daffodils by the springhouse did especially well, blooming naturally in clumps, as we had hoped they would.

More and more the vegetables claimed us. On the 2nd of April, a fortnight late, at least, we put in Blue Bantam peas, seeded in a double row, apple sticks stuck in the ground between them and woven together. Eugene was adept at that. Next 250 two-year asparagus roots, Martha Washington, were planted in the trenches prepared for them. This was followed a day or so later by one row of Detroit Dark Red Short Top beets, one row of Imperator carrots and two rows onion sets, one white, one yellow. To keep the balance straight, we found time, or rather Horace did, to stir up the lawn a bit close to the house, fertilize and feed it. The new myrtle was mulched deeply with peat.

In laying out the vegetable garden, we were drawn between the problem of keeping it handily small and that of having it hold enough to be worthwhile. All work on it

we must do ourselves, with a day now and then when
Horace could help us. Above all, we wanted it practical, of
handy size and no frills in what it produced. The first plot
was roughly the size of the old chicken run—100 by 54
feet. Above it, across a sunken lane where once a farm
track had run, we laid off a second patch for corn and
tomatoes, as soon as we thought that the lower garden
would not be large enough. The upper plot measures 100 by
33 feet. Now, two years gone, we have learned both plots
are too large. Next year we shall cut them down.

We planned the first year to seed lettuce, onions, parsley,
radishes, spinach, beets, peas, carrots, tomatoes, string
beans, bush limas, pole limas, cauliflower, Brussels sprouts,
corn, okra, squash, eggplants, muskmelons, cucumbers,
watermelons and watercress. Rhubarb and asparagus, as has
been said, were put in as plants. The watercress was seeded
first in pans of damp soil, then transplanted to the over-
flow of our springs where they have taken hold nicely. It
is handy to have a supply always fresh for sandwiches or
garnish. Spearmint we had found in abundance here. Some
of it we moved to a cool corner of the terrace, handy for
iced tea or juleps. Our herb bed came later.

As spring drew on and we pressed to keep pace
with it, we were blessed with rain to spare. What a joy it
was to hear it—dropping as the rain, as the small rain
upon the tender herb, and as the showers upon the grass.
What a start that gave the garden against the inevitable
summer drought. While working there in this our first
April, we could hear each morning the ku-kluck of pheasants
on the slopes above us and see them gliding as Garry investigated. Eugene with due excitement counted twenty-
two in one or two nyes.

"Phesan'! Ve eat heem!"

That might be all very well in fall, but hen birds in April were not quite in order.

How fascinating are the terms once used for carving such birds. A pheasant, so we are told by the purist, must be allayed. So must a teal. One should wing a partridge, unbrace a mallard, of course, thigh a woodcock or a curlew, rear a goose, display a crane, dismember a heron and lift a swan! Should you knock over a humble rabbit next year, remember in carving him he is unlaced. So far we have not been embarrassed by a surfeit of these, swans and cranes especially. Just what is done to a peacock in his pride before eating we do not know. Our only peacock is Gabriel Junks and he is of lead. We did, however, begin work on the new terrace wall by poking hen-and-chickens, a different kind of fowl, *Sempervivum tectorum*, into the crannies between the stones, probably more useful than unbracing mallards.

THE COLDFRAME WAS OVERFLOWING as seedlings grew. On the 10th of April, cabbage, cauliflower and eggplant joined the tomatoes there. The cabbage was Savoy Perfection Drumhead; the cauliflower, Burpeeana; the eggplant, Black Beauty. The amount of seed was, of course, surprisingly small. We saw to it that the soil in the coldframe was thoroughly friable and well watered. In the garden itself, though very late, we seeded parsley, Extra Curled Dwarf; radish, Cherry Belle; spinach, America; lettuce, Premium Great Lakes, and, later, Batavian endive.

This was no sooner done than we yielded again to flowers. Fifty more periwinkle went in along the drive, together with 10 rockcress, and 10 stonecrop, above the rebuilt wall. A Carpet of Gold, a Coral Creeper and a *Repens alba* rose were the start of our rose bank-to-be above the drive. Not much, but they showed the way. There

are over a hundred roses there now and we hope there
will be more. We have found that fall planting, especially
of the hardier sorts such as Max Graf, gives a better start
than waiting until spring. Three Rosina and 3 Snow Queen
violets were tucked in under the terrace ha-ha.

We knew we should not do it, but who can stop? Sweet
alyssum and annual candytuft were seeded as edging
around three flower beds we had made by transplanting
phlox, daylilies, tiger lilies, iris and peonies from the old
border beside the asparagus. Two virgin's-bower and 2
Clematis paniculata went in by the steps of the bank.

It did not take us long this first summer to see that we
had overextended ourselves badly. This was inevitable, I
suppose. Wiser and considerably chastened, we regrouped
that fall. The long border, very difficult to tend, was done
away with altogether. Two small permanent beds, half-
moon in shape, the old Spring Bank sundial between them,
were made close in to the terrace, handy to the water tap.
A third bed has been added, a green one, azaleas, laurels
and one Franklin tree for height. These three small beds,
with the borders around the terrace, afford all the colour
we want. Labour in caring for them has been cut to a
minimum. Will we stop here? I doubt it.

IT WAS THE MIDDLE OF APRIL when our seedling
trees unexpectedly arrived from the Department of Forests
and Waters. Five hundred white pine and Norway spruce.
We had looked for them early in March before a rush of
spring work had swamped us. Now we had forgotten all
about them. A hurry call, however, soon brought our faithfuls, Frank and John, reinforced this time by Chuck and
Doc, all husky. Pitching in as two teams, diggers and
planters, they got over 300 trees in by dark. A few days
later, Bill showed up. He and my wife and Eugene put in

the other 200 while I was away. Most of them have lived and are beginning to show a bit.

The onion storm, a light snow on the 14th, surprised us, but should not. It always comes about this time. As the snow melted we ploughed the upper fields. Rain all spring had kept us back for weeks on that. The late snow must have assured the flowers that spring was really here now, for suddenly the flowering quince, the flowering almond and the spice bush, leucothoë, jonquils and snow-flakes blossomed near the terrace, while crocus, daffodils, aconite, jasmine, glory-of-the-snow, snowdrops, grape-hyacinth, blue myrtle, blue squills and forsythia seemed everywhere. In the terrace pots and along the borders were pansies, violas, hyacinths, English daisies, candytuft, violets, heartsease and primroses. The fields and woodland matched them, and better, with bloodroot, the lovely wind-flower, rue anemone, hepaticas and spring-beauty. We must not forget our wild strawberries either.

H o w u n b e l i e v a b l e the pageantry of spring can be. And always new. Then truly the trees of the field clap their hands for joy. One of the loveliest days of all this year was soft with a drift of rain, low clouds seeping through the cleft above Springhead, till our little hills had a touch of highlands about them. Sun, quick-shafted, broke through now and then, touching the young barley to tenderest green, a different green from that of wheat or of rye. Who can resist such a day? In town, no doubt, it was dreary enough. Here it was a joy to see and taste and feel. We took advantage of it to seed some portulaca, the rose moss, in one of the beds and then more carrots, radishes, parsley and beets in the garden. A second row of peas, as well, Fordhook Wonder, this time, was got in, soil ideal for them, with the rain. Rhubarb was well up by now;

asparagus in the old bed thrusting. Wild cherry blow, the mazzard blossoms—"wearing white for Eastertide"—was sweet on the hill above, just to remind us that beauty has its place as well as the more earthy fundamentals. Mustard and yellow rocket had turned wild patches to gold. Groundsel was on its way. On the 18th of April we had our first asparagus. All the labour on that old bed had been repaid.

Snow flurries, then quite a frost on the 22nd, did no harm. We were beginning to learn now how much must be done to land to get anything started. Before we were through, we had ploughed each field, harrowed it, waited till it had been limed, then harrowed it again. Noel was ready to mix seed, mix fertilizer, drill both in and go over every thing with his heavy drag-board. Quantities of lime and fertilizer and seed had been recommended to us by the County Agent and the Soil Conservationist, field by field. They were per acre approximately $1\frac{1}{2}$ tons of lime, 600 pounds of 5-10-10, 8 pounds of brome-grass seed, 14 pounds of alfalfa seed, 4 pounds of timothy seed and one bushel of oats as cover crop. Our plan was to seed this grass mixture for permanent sod, top-dressing twice a year with 300 pounds of 0-20-20, and 30 pounds of borax every four years. This was expensive, so the first year we took on the lower west field only, although we did lime all fields. Noel, in return for the work he did, was given the other fields to plant for himself as he liked; for one year only. He decided on oats but no grass seed for the upper west field, cowpeas in the lower and middle east fields, with corn on the upper field. We hated to take on so little ourselves, but again the budget ruled. As it is, we are behind on our top-dressing. The following autumn we got our second field into winter wheat, however, grass mixture included. And in our second spring we put two more fields into oats with grass mixture. So, little by little, we have worked towards grass and followed the original plan we had set as a goal.

WHILE ALL THIS was going on, dwarf narcissus added its welcome blossoms to the others. To our surprise, an old friend sent us 60 small boxwood bushes which he had grown from slips at Chilton. Some of these were just what we needed to edge our jonquil clusters on either side of the front terrace steps. Others were planted at the back of our three beds to form low hedges there—one day.

Flowers, though few, were really showing now. Peonies were out. Dogwoods had opened, masses of wild ones in unexpected beauty along the edge of the wood beyond the orchard. The old apple tree near the door and its neighbour, the Rusty Coat, were soon covered with blossoms and humming with innumerable bees. We found time somehow to give the apple a blossom spray, two in fact. This paid in apple sauce two months later. A pear tree flowered—one of the dwarfs, as did two of the new cherry trees.

In odd moments, 6 hardy candytuft, iberis, were set in along the edge of the ha-ha, with a columbine or two in the border below it and a virgin's-bower by the bank.

WE WERE LIVING on that little terrace now and have done so ever since. The old bricks have a mellowed patina about them that goes pleasantly with the walls of the house and the new masonry of the library and the ha-ha, where pains were taken to use only weathered stone. At first we were troubled by weeds in the cracks of the bricks, but this was remedied by a trickle of ordinary salt along them. Moss there, yes; grass tufts, no.

Being of a practical mind, Eugene forsook his scything long enough to paint the lower doors of the barn and the great doors of the haymows above an honest red. He then dug a row of holes for dahlias along the side of the garden.

Buttercups and bugs came together. A tent caterpillar is like the wild ass of Uz. He searcheth after every green thing and we soon can tell that he has found it. There seem to be two ways to defeat these pests. Burn every egg mass when leaves are down. Fell every wild cherry tree in sight. We are doing our best at both right now. How odd to think that caterpillar means hairy cat.

BY EARLY MAY, of course, wildflowers had taken over, especially the little ones, often unnoticed, but none the less worthy. Cinquefoil, so like the wild strawberry, ground ivy, stars-of-Bethlehem, shepherd's-purse, greater celandine, jack-in-the-pulpit, sweet rocket, yellow rocket, golden groundsel, May-apple, how heartening it is to see them, especially here, old friends, in new places.

Across the lane, dogwoods in flower clustered where junipers shaded the slope, steep above the mill pool. Few trees are more graceful than a wild dogwood can be when left to its own devices in the shadow of other trees. Set in the open, it rounds out, billowing and matronly, colourful no doubt but still not the lithe and lovely dryad of the forest.

Every day planting went on in the garden, a little at a time:

> Four seeds in a hole,
> One for the rook, one for the crow,
> One to rot and one to grow.

Old-fashioned advice, but worth heeding.

Speaking of things old-fashioned, we shared in a brave sight at the races that May when a coach-and-four drove up to the saddling paddock. Can anything made by man be more satisfying? Sight and sound and motion, there is a glory about it that these days miss. It seems so alive. And how dowered with memory it can be! Who could forget the thrill of climbing Snakehouse Hill from the Rose Tree after races in the old days, cockhorse aiding the four-in-hand uphill? Or long evenings tooling along the Swedesford, bottles of ale cooling in a bucket of oats in the boot? Or on the box-seat beside the driver, swinging out of Windsor Great Park? Such days are golden still.

COACHES OR NO, work went on. We put in a white lilac and a mockorange above the vegetable garden where the old lane goes. A few more tulips appeared to cheer us—Darwin Queen of the Night, a try but too dark for our liking; Glacier, which was lovely; one or two stalwart Marshal Haigs. *Phlox canadensis* filled the narrow borders of the terrace with the coolest of blue. White violets soon joined them. Jetberry flowered under the library window. And bridal-veil—we had cut to two bushes of this. Day-lilies, iris and columbine came into flower with the jet-berry, while black haw brightened the woodland above. Our lilac clumps were masses of colour now and sweet with scent.

Two azaleas, a white and a pink, went in near the chimney end of the house, well shaded by junipers already there. We put a *Centranthus ruber*, Jupiter's-beard, above the ha-ha where it has proved a faithful bloomer ever since. The dahlia row was planted, roots having wintered well, for the most part. More sweet alyssum, maritimum and argenteum, was seeded as edging. Though late for it, plenty of rain encouraged us to scatter grass seed where the lawn seemed sparse. In the truck patch our third double row of peas went in early in May, Fordhook Wonder. We have found, as we did in the past, that peas usually ripen at once, regardless of how carefully we stagger their planting. None of them can stand real heat or drought. Long Island Brussels sprouts, too late, and more beets were also planted now.

By mid-May over fifty sorts of flowers, shrubs and trees had blossomed here, most of them taking us by surprise for we had not dreamed there were so many. We swore we wouldn't, but in went zinnias, French marigolds, corn-flowers, scabiosa, pompon asters, morning-glories, these were to give colour this summer where climbing roses were hoped for later on the house walls. Nasturtiums were seeded above the drive wall, but did not do well there. Too much sun, I dare say, and too dry.

In the coldframe, seedlings no longer, tomatoes were thinned and set out, as were the cabbages. My wife had done wonders with them. On the 16th of May, we seeded one row of bush limas—Fordhook 242, one row of string beans, called bush beans these days, Green Pod Topcrop. Better than that, however, we went to an herb sale.

It was at Bryncoed, not far away, near the Birch Run Valley, where beds and borders and incredible clematis are a foreground of delight to sloping meadows, grazing sheep and the waters of the lake below. Where can so lovely an old house, such wizardry of planting and such kindly hosts be found? The herbs and other plants were on sale in the barn. We bought rosemary, golden thyme, lemon verbena, English lavender, sweet marjoram, rue, chives, basil and tarragon. The proceeds of this annual sale help support the tiny herb garden at the College of Physicians in Phila-delphia, a place of unusual charm to those who know it.

Our own little herb garden is just below the kitchen window and close to the new terrace. Warmed by a summer sun, its scent is like a breath from the Spicy Isles. We now have there in addition to those just mentioned, mint, moved from the brookside, European pennyroyal, American pennyroyal, heliotrope, English thyme and that most useful of herbs—chervil. Not a day passes without some of these finding their toothsome way to iced tea or soup or omelette or salad or even to spring chicken marinated with herbs and olive oil.

COUNTRY HEREABOUTS has held to the old names. They weave for us the pattern of its settling. Bryncoed, Uwchlan and Nantmeal, obviously are Welsh, showing where the Welsh Tract extended northward. Pickering, Coventry, Charlestown and Vincent, St. Mary's and Warwick are English. Our own township of Pikeland goes back some 250 years. In those days it was called Newington for Stoke Newington in Middlesex. The original grant, however, was held by a man named Joseph Pike. His name endured, but the name of his home in England faded from mind. Some of the smallest hamlets here, hidden in the hills, have lovely names and are even lovelier themselves. Merlin by its cider mill means the blue pigeon hawk, the smallest of the falcons. It, too, has a Welsh flavouring, for was not Myrddin a Welshman, our Merlin, King Arthur's wizard? Solid Pennsylvania-Dutch names creep into the north and the west. Ludwig's Corner, Knauertown and the like. It is fascinating to read history, the truest history, from a chance signpost at the turning of a lane, for such things stem from the people.

IT MUST HAVE BEEN the middle of May when we found enough lull to make, paint and set up rose trellises on the walls. Climbers there were none, but a hope was there—since fulfilled for the roses have come. It all takes time. Our clock in these fields is one of flowers, telling us not of hours but of the sure sweet cycle of the year. Blackberries blossoming, false Solomon's-seal, bracken almost as high as the old stone wall below the spring, warned us that mid-May was passing. Clusters of daylilies and iris showed in hidden corners, later than their fellows in the sun. High time to plant a perennial bleeding heart by the terrace and transplant a spade or two of forget-me-nots from the brook to the springhouse. They have rooted there cheerily, liking wet feet.

Our first peas blossomed on May 22nd, encouraged by rain and cool weather. A less appealing sight was a tangled mass of poison ivy among the climbing roses at the house end of the drive. These were old ones, here when we came. We could not spray the poison ivy without destroying or injuring the roses. So in we dug and spaded out *Toxidendron radicans,* roots and all. A good scrubbing with hot water and brown kitchen soap in the shower served to forestall trouble. Time is the essence.

E U G E N E , bless his stubborn soul, was a perfectionist when it came to putting in lima-bean poles. Each butt must be sharpened to a precise point.

"The root—eet help eet."

Perhaps it does. The poles must be almost two feet in the ground. No use arguing. I tried to explain what lima-bean vines were like.

"One metre! In groun'—one metre! Uhgh! A leetle less."

"But limas aren't that heavy."

"In Ukraine—one metre—"

Maybe he thought we were planting hops for beer. In

any event, those poles were reared for the ages. It took a pick and shovel in the fall to pry them loose.

Poles in, we planted six seeds to a hill, thinning them later to four. Burpee's Big 6, they were.

In the flower beds, sweet alyssum, with *Sedum acre* in the terrace wall cracks, had flowered. More zinnias, standbys no weather can defeat, were seeded as late as the 1st of June.

As May neared its end, wildflowers and cultivated raced side by side in our affections. Daisies, the hawkweeds, king-devil, heal-all, wild sorrel, dewberry, the later violets, basil, woody nightshade, bedstraw, scarlet pimpernel, yarrow, moneywort, daisy-fleabane, a little early, tufted vetch, Deptford pinks, moth-mullein, campion, dogbane, horse-nettle, most horrible of pests, growing everywhere, deep-rooted, indestructible, all the clovers, melilot and the rest, blue-eyed grass, speedwell, with the sturdier growth of high summer, were taking over now.

In May we put in a small floribunda rose by the corner of the terrace. It was the most delicate shell-pink in colour, flowering steadily till frost. We wish we knew its name. Always in blossom, never leggy, just a low delightful cluster of bloom for seven months of the year. Also it has wintered well in place. It came to us from Chilton. Nothing more lovely could add colour to the ha-ha.

Fruit trees had been sprayed as noted, but lush spring grass can fairly smother the smaller saplings. We saw to it now that these trees had a weeding around their stocks. Care was taken to keep them mulched all summer. Also we watered them as well as we could when the drought struck. It is the first year after planting that counts. That safely passed, with any luck most of them seem able to fend for themselves. In spite of our watering, one peach, a Hale Haven, died that summer. We replaced it last autumn with a Golden Jubilee.

OUR FIRST THREE ROWS of sweet corn, Iochief,
went in the 28th of May. The transplanted Pritchard Certi-
fied tomatoes, moved by my wife from the coldframe, did
famously. They had been moved late but soon made up
for it.

Horace is a great one for transplanting. Not sure of our
handiwork with the lima beans, he had seeded some of his
own choosing in a little coldframe he improvised from a
window sash. Now at the month's end he transplanted 48
plants to our poles. We had to admit they were sturdier
than those sowed there. Four good plants to the pole seemed
about right.

First beets, tiny, but tender, first carrots, lettuce and
rhubarb had come by Memorial Day. We had been enjoying the radishes since April. Most of these seeds had been
got in too late, but our first spring was difficult and constant rain had delayed us.

We have since found that one secret of early vegetables
and surely of tender ones is to mulch each row as soon as
the seeds are up, thus keeping the early moisture in the
ground, well to the surface where the short rootlets need it.
For mulch, we used Eugene's scythings, a great stack of
them carefully salvaged. It seems to do the trick. Roots,
such as beets and carrots, are vastly improved by this, for
they can grow in soft soil not be gripped in hardened,
sun-baked clay, as is often their fate.

WHILE MOVING SPEARMINT to the herb bed, we
put in a spadeful or so below the springhouse and outside
the barnyard wall where we knew it would spread, for we
love the fresh, cool fragrance of it, especially in deep summer after showers. The cottage of Arley close by is gay
with sweet rocket in May. Our neighbours there let us move
a little of it to the front of our springhouse where it is

spreading. It has to be watched, of course, but some is lovely.

Roses clambering over a great rock did not wait till June, but bloomed before the Loddon lilies had podded below them. New multiflora roses, the start of a little hedge east of the springhouse, also blossomed early. It was now that the great cascade of roses, growing wild across the creek, opened overnight. Alena was impressed, French and German mixed, as she gazed at them.

"Ah! Ah! Missus! Wi elegant! Thees rose—ah! Wunderbar! A parc we haf!"

Eugene was loath to commit himself. Perhaps no roses grow wild in the Ukraine. Besides, he was never a man for a hubbub.

"The hay appeareth and the tender grass sheweth itself."

4

CROWN OF THE YEAR

THE TENDER GRASS sheweth itself, so we are told, but there was no hay save in our dreams, and as for tender grass the toughest of ragweed and burdock had taken over wherever we had not ploughed. In that ploughing, of course, lay our hope, for beyond it under the springing cover of oats we were counting on grass. What Noel accomplished that spring made us grateful. At sixteen, with his tractor, his two ploughs and his harrow, he was well on the way towards transforming the place. Only in his first seeding was he helped for a while by his father who mixed the seed and fertilizer for him. After that he was on his own.

Through all the bustle of seed-drilling, weeks later, we still were drawn to the old asparagus bed that has so bountifully rewarded us. We stopped cutting early in June that spring to spare it. In payment for the feasts it had given, we put on 60 pounds of 5-10-5. The stalks were a bit low yet for mulching and we were waiting for a good soaking rain. But we did let it go comfortably to seed.

IN THE FLOWER BEDS that was just what we tried not to do. Deadheads were nipped from daylilies, iris and peonies regularly. This doesn't take very long, now and then, in beds and clumps as small as ours, but it surely helps appearances and often encourages more bloom later on, especially with things like phlox. The long border, since abandoned, was more trouble than all the rest.

Very early in June we seeded 1 row of Clemson Spineless okra and 6 hills of Netted Gem muskmelons. The okra, as often happens, was far too thickly sown. Later we thinned it to about 8-9 inches between plants. The quantity of okra we got was a pleasing surprise, lasting till frost and giving us plenty to freeze for the winter. What is more tasty on a nippy day than chicken gumbo, homemade, well laced with okra?

IN THE FRONT of our flower beds, space had been left as usual for annuals. Here we seeded asters, the hardy sorts, pompon asters, summer chrysanthemums, zinnias, especially the cut-and-come-again kind. These proved useful in the doldrums of summer. Zinnias once were called Old Maids. They may not be the most graceful of flowers, but to see them undaunted by heat, careless of drouth, stiff and defiant of aphids and beetles, is a comfort when all else wilts. Their colouring these days surely is wide enough in range to please anybody's taste. One can do worse in a garden than give them their due. The secret lies in not having too many in one place, with some discrimination in

size and variation of it, coupled with the right colours
where you want them.

OUR DAYS WERE DIVIDED now between borders
and truck patch, little time to one, much to the other. It is
in June that the battle of the weeds must be won if ever.
After that they cause little trouble. A routine was soon
worked out whereby a certain number of rows, usually
two, were weeded and cultivated each morning before the
sun grew hot. This was not difficult. It took little time, far
under an hour. In a fortnight or less the garden had been
covered with no hardship at all. Regularity does it.

Next time round, we found the soil still loose and friable
and weeds negligible, except for the horror of the ground-
cherry or horse-nettle, one of the nightshades. It seems quite
impossible to eradicate. In our early cultivating, most rows
were well hoed up, especially corn, bush beans and limas.
This seems to protect their roots. Beets and carrots and
onions, however, we did not hoe up very much. Instead
the soil around them was kept well loosened. The trick
with them apparently is a mulching of straw or grass clippings. Mention has been made of the change that was made.
The first year, in spite of our cultivating, both beets and
carrots were too firmly set in the hard ground. We could
not pull them without getting a handful of top greens but
no carrot. Often we had to spade them up. There is little
of that now under mulch, although this spring has been
far drier. We are six inches short of rain already according
to the charts.

Dusting in the vegetable garden began early and was
continued until September, a miserable chore but essential.
We used the Du Pont All Purpose dust on everything when
plants were small except on tomatoes and eggplants. These
were dusted with Du Pont special tomato and eggplant

preparation. Later, when the vegetables had formed, we dusted almost everything every other week with rotenone. Red Arrow spray was used on all beans against the bean beetle. A circle of 5 per cent DDT was laid around each tomato plant, cabbage, broccoli and cauliflower when first set out from the coldframe. This soon put an end to cutworms.

The first day we were dusting, Garry marched up and down the garden several rows off. Then, to our horror, he suddenly collapsed. The vet pulled him round, but it was a close-run thing, as Wellington said after Waterloo. Garry had seemed well away from any possible dust drift, but we had been foolish. Now the garden is *verboten*. Also when we spray poison ivy or rampant honeysuckle, Garry is kept indoors. It is the methexychlor in the spray that does the mischief.

HONEYSUCKLE IS A SNARE. A little of it seems so lovely in the spring. Once out of control, it can become the worst pest in the countryside, edging greedily at the borders of a field, spreading from fence lines, smothering even large trees until they die. Yet again, the breath of it some fine June day in the sweet of the year tempts us despite ourselves. What this side of paradise can be quite so prodigal of scent? Going up our hill to see what damage honeysuckle was doing to the woodland, I realized this as fragrance from the slope swept down to me in the cool fresh weather long before I reached it. Wild strawberries were at their prime. I found a perfectly good cherry tree, to boot, hidden in a hedgerow, hung with fruit. We'd had no hint that it was there. One joy of the farm has been the amazing number of secrets it keeps to be discovered, one by one, when least expected. Coming down to the barn, I checked more flowers that had answered last night's rain, coreopsis, beard-tongue, pimpernel, daisy-fleabane, moneywort.

That evening, to prove that spring had gone, first fireflies twinkled on the lawn. Where have they been since last September? Miss Lingard phlox showed white in the borders. The Kousa dogwood and the Japanese hollies were in blossom. White geraniums, white vinca, white begonias, white petunias were cool on the terrace. Red geraniums, fuchsia, ageratum, marigolds and bleeding hearts added a brighter touch. Pansies and violas, faithful since April, were moved, still blooming, to the shade of the lilacs. It was the 7th of June.

Next day we put in 1½ rows of corn and set out 16 cauliflowers—Burpeeana. Time had come to stake tomatoes, 55 of them. Tying up the vines was begun. It seems to help tomatoes to strip the lower shoots for almost a foot up the stems. It was the 12th of June when we had first peas, very late really but a thrill. Spinach and carrots came a day or so later. Soon we put in one short row of Dixie Queen watermelon, some more muskmelons and Burpee's cucumber Extra Early White Spine and Fordhook Pickling, with a row of Early Prolifio Straightneck squash. It proved too late, however, for all except the cucumbers and squash. Lack of rain gave them little chance. Old folk say that squash should go in with the first of the apple blossoms. They are right. All through the year our luck held to the average and we were thankful. A failure here; perhaps a success or two there. We knew that we were lucky.

Though late, we did risk planting some chrysanthemums in one of the borders. These were plants not seeds. They have done well, not exciting but adequate.

JUNE 16TH MARKED one year since we had begun work here. Much had been done, that was obvious, but only the merest scratch had been made in what remained. That is as it should be. We were beginning to know now where flowers would show, for we had seen them a year ago. Yarrow was in blossom. A matrimony-vine clambering to the eaves of the barn had flowered. The later tall day-lilies were out as were hollyhocks, many of them showing in unexpected places. Loddon Gold was true to its name, great masses flourishing in the borders. These were on the bright side. Really cleaning the barn, from stalls to hay-mows, was not so easy. A ton or so of rubbish was lugged out, burned or carted away, yet nothing was put to waste. Whatever could be used as firewood, especially as kindling, was saved. Eight tons of crushed limestone were used at this time as a new foundation for stalls and sheeppen. This layer of stone was covered with six inches of clay well tamped.

To celebrate the anniversary of our purchase here, we asked our good friends the Vails from Chester Springs to tea. It was Albert Vail who had recalled my riding by so many years ago. Mrs. Vail gave us some lupines from her garden to plant in ours. They were lovely. Better gardeners do not come than the Vails. Friends from Pippin Hill soon joined us. All were those who had known the country in the old days before the nightmare of hard roads, ranch types and superhighways had been dreamed of. What a different world it is today, but never a lost one. How strange to think that in one life's span I have seen wheat cradled with a scythe and sheaves tied with a twist of straw as men had been doing for a thousand years. How seldom nowadays does one pass grain in shocks or stooks, as they were some-times called. Obviously the use of the corn-picker and the combine and all farm machinery is a godsend.

It is ridiculous to worship the labour and sweat of the past just for the past's sake. Most who do have never tried it. Like Miniver Cheevy, child of scorn, they sigh for what is not and curse the commonplace. The skill that went with handcraft, however, is a different matter. We must bow to that despite the labour. As a boy, I used to watch with wonder, the shocks going up by hand behind the reaper-and-binder, each shock different in its kind. Nine bundles to an oats shock, grain heads up. Twelve bundles to the wheat shock, heads up. Four bundles topping each shock, spread and pressed down, thatchwise, never tied, at just the right angle. They called these bundles the bonnet or cap.

How tragic it could be to see acres of oats, soil well tilled, grain well seeded, a good harvest safely cut, but still a-field, then a week of rain setting each shock to sprouting till all were green and sodden. Hay in cocks often suffered the same fate. Combining has saved that heartbreak. Only last evening we raced a storm threat here at Melbrook, clearing eight acres of oats till all were bagged in time and in the barn. The past has much to be proud of, but there's plenty of life in the old world yet. We owe a debt to every new invention that has helped men on the land, for most of us like to see the day's stint speeded.

ONE OF THE MOST INCREDIBLE things about trying to grow anything is the persistence of life itself. No better place can show this than a farm. It may seem difficult at times to start things growing, but it is vastly more difficult to kill them. One day in our first spring here we noticed that an old grapevine by the terrace had sent up shoots. When the terrace had been built, that vine was removed to make room for foundations. We had dug deeply until every vestige of root had been grubbed up. Or so we thought. Now a year later here it was forcing its way through heavy stones as spry as ever. This time we pried even deeper and did get it out—a six-inch fragment of root stock that was replanted with our new grapevines above the barn. Long since it has outstripped them, as vigorous and hearty as the best.

Again, yesterday, we had another example of life's tenacity. Coming down from the wheat field as harvesting ended, I took Garry, still a puppy in his ways, for a dip in the stream, his surest delight. Suddenly he came out of the water with a young wild duck, a scaup it was, tight in his jaws. Now Garry, among his virtues, loves to retrieve. Among his foibles—our fault—he will bring anything to us on the run but he hates to deliver it. He did not crush the poor duck but he held fast to it. Instinct not training served him there, but I could not get the poor duck free, although it was perfectly motionless. In fact, I thought at first that Garry had killed it. In the end I lured him into plunging after a stick tossed in the water, thus getting a chance to grab at the scaup which he had dropped. Only then did I discover its real plight.

Some thoughtless fool had lost or left a fishing lure, probably along the bank. It was a horrible plastic thing, three inches long, crimson in colour, hung with three hooks, all trebles. A forty-pound salmon could be killed with it and that, too, would be a murder not sport. What use it could possibly be in this little brook, it is hard to imagine. The duck must have stepped on or swum into it. One of the barbed hooks had pierced the gristle of the off foot's webbing. Two more points were embedded high up on the thigh, distorting and bending the poor creature's leg so that it could neither swim nor walk nor take off in flight. A pitiable sight.

My wife, quick in emergencies, worked the devilish hooks free, the duck never stirring. I think it knew we were trying to help it for it never winced. The moment it was clear of the barbs, it just ruffled its feathers, then settled sleek and snug in my hands. I carried it to the stream quickly and slid it into the water where it dove instantly, as wild ducks will, swimming underwater far downstream to emerge with scarcely a ripple close to the far bank where spatterdocks gave covert. What that helpless bird had gone through we could not know. It may have been clutched in the hooks for days. Garry's mouthing had not been gentle. Again we had seen the unbelievable hold on life that nature gives to all. But I'd like to meet the heartless oaf who left the hooks there, either knowingly or not. Children wade and swim in that reach of the brook. They, too, could have stepped on the nine-barbed horror.

Speaking of ducks, how can a web-footed duck find perch high in a birch tree? And take off from there in flight? One did so this morning. I marvelled at the grace and the balance of it.

But we are ahead of ourselves. A year back the garden was keeping us busy, not ducks, as we twined up the vines of the lima beans. We had five rows of string between poles. Brussels sprouts were being hoed. We were weeding and cultivating between the rows of lettuce and spinach, beets and carrots. Beans needed thinning. Why is it that beans, especially, are always planted too thickly? Garry, too, was adding to our chores those summer days by digging himself cool hideaways under the particular shrubs we loved the best. Now and then he varied this by excavating a series of holes in the lawn where he could lie at his ease like a dusting hen. We had to fill the shrub holes quickly. Even a good-sized holly can be killed once its roots are laid bare. The foxholes in our pleasance are there yet, I'm sorry to say, some of them at least. It seems a labour of Sisyphus to fill them in.

Watering in June, where flowers or new shrubs are concerned, can never be overlooked. Boxwood, ivy shoots, the Kousa dogwood, Washington thorn, cherry laurel, the two transplanted hollies, the two junipers, seemed to need it. We had learned long ago in watering new plantings of wall ivy to turn the hose on the wall above the ivy's immediate reach and let the water trickle down. In the end it reaches the roots all right, but the dampened stone above seems to encourage growth upward.

ON THE HILL, Midsummer's Day, wild roses sweetened the slope. We had no hint that they were there, abounding by the corner of a hedgerow. Black-eyed Susan, milkweed, red clover, yellow hop-clover, Queen Anne's lace, elderberry, knotweed, St. John'swort, yellow avens, hidden catnip, all were in flower by now. We liked them as much as the best in the borders. Besides it was pleasant to see them against a background of wild strawberries and blackberries ripe for the picking.

Eugene and Alena accepted the strawberries as *fraises de bois*. But as for the blackberries, they would not touch them.

"Nein, Missus! Nein! Ve not eat eet. These not good for eat. You see."

No use arguing. Perhaps they thought they were poison ivy in fruit. We ate them ourselves. Good old Eugene had a directness about him that I liked. When in despair I'd ask him what he did like, he never lacked answer.

"Svine! Vy not? My fader he haf' twendy svine! Und one horse. Here ve haf' no svine. Eet iss not right."

No question about Eugene's not standing in the old ways or asking for the old paths. He knew where the good way was and nothing could swerve him.

Whenever a lull came in our work, he would look hopefully towards the barn.

"You'd better rest a bit now," I'd tell him. "It's hot."

"Nock! Nock! I mak' eet queek in barn-house—for svine! Much svine! You see!"

They have not come yet, those swine, but that was not Eugene's fault. He did his best.

IT WAS MID-JUNE when we mulched salt hay on the old asparagus bed, the stalks being tall enough not to be smothered. It worked. Two more rows of corn went in on the 22nd. We picked a bushel of peas that day, eating many and freezing more. Rain had brought the oats on nicely. Watercress had blossomed by the spring. We were content.

Our garden, even at the start, depended on mulching. We found a mulch particularly useful around rhubarb, holding moisture there. Nothing has swayed us from our faith in mulches and organic fertilizing of the soil, but so far we have still felt it necessary to use some chemical fertilizer and some dusts and sprays. Perhaps in time, when we have ploughed under more of the mulches and kept on manuring, the need for chemical aids may lessen. Already, we are depending on less 5-10-5 in planting vegetables than we used before our manure and mulches and rye turned under had begun to take effect. In the fields themselves, so terribly starved, we are using all that we can afford—lime, 5-10-10, borax and the rest. Had we tons of manure available, we'd plough every bit of it under. Old-fashioned, but still the best to our way of thinking.

Some things help that we do have. This very week, as an example, we had weeded, then cultivated the space where the double rows of peas had been. Then we got our young friend Bill from the Corner to dig into two of our compost piles, rotted leaves mostly, and cover the whole pea area several inches deep with leaf mould. This will spare the soil a blistering of August sun. In fall, ploughed under, with all the manure we can muster, it should help build up organic content. A good liming should offset any leaf acidity present.

THE FIRST FRUIT that came to us in quantity was the apple drop from the old Yellow Transparent by the drive. The tree had not been sprayed very much, I dare say, in the past, but we had managed to give it one scale and two blossom sprays in this our first spring. The fruit from that one tree and the apple sauce it made were amazing. This year we sprayed again properly. It would be hard to count the apples we have gathered—not a wormy one in the lot. We must have given over fifteen bushels away to friends and still we have more than we can use. Each laden branch is propped securely. Otherwise the tree would have broken. From the apple beside it, very old, but also sprayed—is it a Rusty Coat?—we are making apple jelly, a mixture of Yellow Transparent and some of the other producing the best results. The precise proportion seems to be one of the guarded arcana of the kitchen.

The last half row of bush limas and half row of lettuce were seeded towards the end of June, probably too hot for the lettuce, but watering nursed them along. String beans were in flower. We knew how quickly they would pod after that. First onions had come to table. Morning-glories and abelia, rosemoss and nasturtiums, mint and watercress were blossoming. Chicory bordered the lane with blue—till sun was hot. Thimbleweed showed on the hill.

My wife and I, cheered by what the garden was doing, made looking at the oats and cowpeas our excuse for cold supper on the hill one evening, all the sweep of the uplands spread before us. Ripening wheat, the deepest ruddy gold, oats, uncut, a lighter gold, barley already in stubble, still a different yellow, the well-loved woodlands between—Patrick's Hill and the L-shaped wood, Sunbury and West

Meadows and Spring Hill—it was worth our climb to see them. Surely these fields were joyful in their summer glory. It was cool on Melbrook Hill, a fair breeze stirring. We picked blackberries for dessert, as a family of woodchucks stood on their hunkers to watch us from the hedgerow below.

I came up next afternoon with a gun, but that was a gesture only. Long before I got anywhere near the hole, the varmity fellow on picket had whistled derisively and bolted the lot of them.

EARLY IN JUNE we built two simple trellises for grapevines, four cedar posts with four slats to each. Three vines to a trellis. We celebrated the eve of the Fourth with first string beans. The garden was our larder now and has remained so ever since, summer and winter, thanks to deep-freeze and lockers.

HOW MIRACULOUS IT IS that nature never exhausts her surprises. Coming home from supper at the Eagle one day, we saw a double rainbow high-arched and splendid, stretching from Bacton Hill towards Charlestown Wood over the fields of wheat and pastures where cattle grazed after milking. It had been intensely hot, then fresh suddenly, clearing after rain. Never before had either my wife or I noticed that the colors are reversed in a double rainbow, showing in one order in the upper spectrum, the opposite below. We have not yet made out whether there is a pot of gold under each arc. Or at which end.

WORK THERE WAS A-PLENTY, but time for a canter on the hills an hour or so almost every morning early before it grew too hot. One could scent the growing corn now, so different in flavour from the nutty breath of wheat. How corn loves the warmer nights. Alfalfa, with its own fragrance, had been cut before this. Clover, dew still on it, is the sweetest of them all. It, too, was in by now. But corn under summer sun is richest in memory, taking one back to pony-cart days. To ride these woodland ways, rich with fairy candles withers high, and meadow rue and mullein and the gold of the evening primrose, to catch the sudden view from Ice Dam Wood towards Fox Hollow, farmland and meadow below, or far across Spruce Haven and the Quiet Valley is to share in paradise. Popping a handy horse over a rail or so adds zest even in summer.

One day Orville the huntsman was with me as we came to a single bar, a sapling green and whippy, fastened high across the ride. Orville, on a green and nervous colt, never batted an eye. It was delight to see the old man gather the youngster perfectly in hand, hocks well under, then pop him over that tricky bar before the horse had a chance to get the wind up. Only those who have known what a green sapling will do in the way of a fall can appreciate the quiet skill, the courage of it. I wish I had measured that bar's height in the wood across from Charlestown. They called the village there Hard Scrabble in the old days. No lovelier can be found in all our hills.

At home, everything seemed blossoming—rose-of-Sharon, hummingbirds poised in midsummer magic, gaillardia, phlox, scabiosa—why such an appalling name?—plantain lilies, cornflowers—each year these seem a deeper blue— Loddon Gold, our summer standby, candytuft, coming and going in the verges till frost, zinnias, far too many, but we were grateful none the less. For the first of the Japanese beetles we were not so grateful, yet in the end they were reasonably few. First cabbages were ready by the 10th of July. We had apparently defeated the cutworms.

PERHAPS OUR GREATEST FIND that summer was the Dobson brothers, all of them, Bob, Gerrit, John and Kenny, ranging in age from seventeen to seven. Bob, the leader, manages his team with firmness, affection and pride. Even Kenny runs a power mower, although he has to reach straight up to grip the handles. Now and then as he trots behind it, he sings and dances a bit to himself. This so fascinates Garry that he, too, joins in, dancing along behind the boy. If watched, both of them instantly stop. It helps to have so much lightheartedness about. We owe more than we can repay to our friends the Dobsons.

As the garden came more into production, our tiny herb bed matched it. Sweet marjoram was in flower. And basil. And, of course, the mint. It was thanks to it that my wife provided us with a punch always delicious, mild or not so mild, according to taste. It consisted of cold tea, sugar, lemon, lots of mint, sherry and rum, with cracked ice. The secret lay in a nice balance between sherry and rum. A glass or two soothed one's point of view considerably. Drought and the heat and the woes of the world outside of our little valley seemed for the nonce less insistent. That punch seemed to go especially well on the cool, bricked terrace.

As oats harvest neared, Eugene scythed a cleared space around each fruit tree so that the cutter-bar would not venture too near. Rabbits had spared these young trees all winter, but were not above nibbling a cabbage now and again in summer. Apparently rotenone is not a deterrent. While seeing to the cabbages, my wife found time somehow, busy as she was each moment, to tie the cauliflower leaves into sunbonnet hoods over the heads now forming. Cauliflowers must be shaded in this way or they will turn yellow and tend to shrivel. As our tomatoes grew, we soon were using all the available rags to tie them to their stakes.

Wide strips from worn-out sheets and pillow cases were the most useful as they did not cut the tomato stems.

Great heat made watering a must. But it also made our poison-ivy spraying far more effective. During midsummer part of one afternoon a week was allotted to this. It did not take long to show results. We have destroyed all of it, for good apparently, in and around the house and barn and garden. This year our attack has been extended far up the lane and is succeeding.

It rained all night and part of the morning, breaking the drought on the 23rd. Though far too late, we seeded a final row of Iochief corn and some lettuce. We also took advantage of the rain to seed hollyhocks for transplanting later. Now just a year later, they are lovely here and there about the barn. This year we have already seeded more of them so as to plant the springhouse wall, old-fashioned but sure of their place in our hearts.

After rain, when prolonged heat has broken, how new a day can be and how cool, the sky as blue as in October, white-flecked with drifts of cloud or high-piled cumuli, a foretaste of the fall. It was wheat harvest now, really the crown of the year, stubble everywhere. Only corn still to come with the second cutting of alfalfa. I rode one day along the ridge above Cricket Hill. Goldfinches were flitting along the hedgerow in their undulating up-and-down way, just in front as we trotted on. For over a mile they kept us cheery company. How much of life flows from the little things. How varied a pattern each day weaves. Squash was ripe in the garden and we'd had first lima beans already. Butter-and-eggs were flowering, and jewelweed in the hollows. Ironweed, bull thistle, tall Aaron's-rod, wild senna, dayflowers, sunflowers, vervain, coneflowers, bouncing Bet, Joe-pie, butterflyweed, goldenrod, all hinted of the fall. But sunflowers, Joe-pie and goldenrod called the tune, as cattle browsed by the hedgerows, seeking shade.

ONE THING HAD TO BE PLANNED for in time. How
to bulldoze out two hedges dividing our east fields into
patches unhandy for working. Cowpeas were there now, but
by fall the hedges must go. Arrangements for this were
made late in July over Exton way. Though far from hedgerows and their bulldozing, one chore seems never to end.
It is watching for off-colour phlox in the borders and pulling
it out. We like all phlox to be white, from Miss Lingard in
the spring on to midsummer phlox and second blooming
later. To keep phlox white one must be vigilant. We can't
be queasy about it. None must go to seed. That is the theory.
In practice, some seeding always occurs and up come the
magentas to wanton all over the border. So we nip off deadheads and pull up by-blows whenever we see them. The
Washington thorn showed signs of aphids about this time,
so we gave it a spray of nicotine sulphate and soap—to
make it stick.

VARIETY IS INFINITE. Having a rather hard fall
on a jut of a boulder while riding over the boughs of a
fallen tree that had blocked my path, I was cured more
quickly than I deserved by good Orville's horse balm. Potent is the word, but effective.

   That very night at 4 A.M. two cows and a calf from a
neighbour's meadow marched up to our terrace, exploring
the bricks but luckily sparing our border flowers. They also
spared the nearby oats, in payment for trespass leaving a
considerable supply of organic fertilizer.

GARRY DISGRACED HIMSELF, for at the very first
moo he fled in terror to his house and never came out
until morning. My wife and I got the truants off towards
the barn till our good neighbours, informed of their where-

abouts, had a chance to retrieve them. The oats, so spared, were combined the last day of July. The first harvest bagged well, considering the condition of the soil. We had started from scratch and no mistake.

To celebrate our harvest home I went cub-hunting with Orville, early in the season as it was. We drew the woodland coverts by Phoenix Hill and soon had found a leash of foxes, two leggy cubs and a vixen, rattling them up and down the forest rides till sun grew hot and scent failed. From the foxes' point of view, they probably relished their morning's workout as much as we did, for they must have known there was no need whatever for hurry. Coming home, I found the garden waiting as usual. Onions and beets must be weeded. Tomatoes were ripe for picking. Beds and borders cried for watering. So did the place where our second coldframe was to go.

Long drouth had turned the ground there to rock. We soaked it for two days with the hose so that Horace might stand some chance against it with his pick. In the end that baked ground balked him. A foot or two down, he had to give it up. Bill, more youth to his credit, had a go at it next. It nearly defeated him, but he stuck at it four feet down, stones as well as hard ground to cope with. The pit was lined on the bottom with fine-meshed wire, its sides laid up with cinder blocks like the first coldframe, then filled with topsoil and manure. I'll wager Bill will not soon forget the hours he spent with pick and shovel in that broiling hole.

We had many helpers now on call, an hour perhaps, one day, then nobody for a week or more, but they were usually ready to help when asked. Horace, wise in the ways of all growing things, came maybe once a fortnight. Bob Dobson and his team saw to the grass. Sam, Bill and Clarence from the Corner helped us from time to time. Clarence, aged eleven, was our mainstay that year at picking beans and limas.

EARLY IN AUGUST great happiness came to us from the visit of a friend from North Carolina. He had served with me faithfully in the war overseas, driving our jeep for endless miles under the most appalling conditions. Everything that came he took with a smile. I owe far more than I could ever repay to him. Naturally, no one could have been more welcome for I had not seen him for years. Okra proved his specialty. In no time he had thinned ours to proper shape, a lesson not forgotten this year. While at the okra, we lifted onions and stored them for the winter. First sweet corn came on August 7th. Cucumbers were not very good, but we were flooded with tomatoes now. Before we were through, we had some three hundred quarts of tomatoes and tomato juice stored for the winter and to share with our friends.

It was at this time that rhubarb was given a booster of 5-10-5 by way of side feeding, scratched in after rain. The old mulch of dried grass and salt hay was put back in time to keep the surface moist. It was hard to imagine that on the 10th of August we had lived a full year here. A busy year, indeed, but rewarding, each day rich with happiness and challenge. There could be no settling on the lees for us.

WE HAD LEARNED a lot in one year. Probably most useful has been the lesson of not tackling too much at once. We knew when it was time to draw stumps and call it an inning. For example, we began to shorten the long border by the asparagus bed. And that led us wisely to abandon it altogether, as we have said, saving the best of its perennials. Daylilies and blue flags were clumped near some lilacs and by the barnyard wall. Our two small permanent beds were already full. While doing this, we separated plantain lilies and set them out. Funkia is dependable as a filler in the shady spots. Its green and white leaves are cool and lasting.

A HARD DAY in field or garden adds zest to our evenings. How lucky we are that the terrace, tucked in the angle of the house walls, looks to sunsets and the west. It is beautiful here and softly green in summer up the slope beyond the bridge. That first twelfthmonth's end, we knew there was a balm a-plenty in Gilead, so heartening it was just to rest there, my wife and I, with new borders and greener fields in the planning. A good book to read, old pipe to puff, then far on the hill, as sunset faded, the sharp-pitched barking of a fox or the ku-kluck of a cockbird stirring—what more could soul desire?

It is not so good to settle too comfortably, of course. Against any such chance, however, the groundhogs decided in mid-August that the best meal of all was an ear of corn. We never saw them at it, but both groundhog and skunk are clever in bending down a stalk of just the right size and clambering up it, as it flattens, until they reach the ripened ear. Actually we lost very little of our sweet corn, but a lot of the field corn was destroyed in this way. Such marauders, if left unbridled, can do untold damage.

It was too bad about the corn, but Noel and young Clarence were gluttons for work as they raked oats straw into golden windrows for baling. There was a good crop of oats and a fine lot of straw even if corn did fare badly.

From time to time, we weeded persistent grass from the young fruit trees, as we had done in the spring, always soaking them well before re-covering with mulch. Fortu-

nately our hose reached from the terrace tap to the furth-
est tree.

WE NEVER LOOK at our orchard-to-be without thinking of Eugene. Our first fall here we were busy one day
putting wire screening around each sapling to save bark
from rabbits. Eugene knew all about that. When the wire
arrived, scratching my battered car still more, as wire will,
the old man shook his head.

"Too short! Ach, nein! Ich say eet vill not do."

"It's three feet high. What rabbits can top that?"

"Nock! Nock! Too lettle eet iss! Two metre we mus' haf."

"That's more than six feet! The trees aren't that high."

Argument with Eugene was on a losing wicket. We'd
learned that by now.

"Two metre!" He could be terse.

"But why?"

"Eet iss so. One metre—snae! So high. Harr, he walk on
snae. Yes? That iss one metre! No? You understan'? In
Ukraine eet is alway so. One metre more we vire an' harr
he cannot reach. Two metre so eet iss."

"We'll never have that much snow here."

Eugene eyed me with pity, a sort of *si jeunesse savait*
look.

"Snae—one metre! Always one metre!"

The branches of the little trees settled the matter. We
could not cut them off or squeeze them into six feet of
screen. The three-foot wire went around them. Eugene mut-
tered to himself all day. Compromise was not his *métier*.
Alena came out to console him with a jug of his favourite
grapefruit juice.

"*Conservatif!* My husban' he not like to change. But snae
—one metre? I do not theenk eet. Much hot ve haf' here."

As a matter of fact, she was right. We had one snowfall

scarcely three inches. How Eugene reconciled this with his
views on the ecology of hares I do not know.

FOR SOME TIME my wife and I had in mind a bed
of old-fashioned roses, those on record as grown in Colonial
gardens. It was fascinating to learn, for instance, what had
been used at Mount Vernon in Washington's time. Authentic records exist. Further downriver is Gunston Hall where
my grandmother lived before the Civil War. We searched
the records and found what had been planted before the
Revolution in the great gardens there where boxwood
towers overhead. Old Scotch, the Moss Rose, the Provence,
Marie Tudor, Rosa Mundi and Damascus were our choice.
Harrison's Yellow we put in by mistake. It is an old type of
rose, a fine one, but not really Colonial in vintage.

To do the work right, we called on good Bill again, our
digger indefatigable. He is taking a premed course at college. Should he become a surgeon, we hope we have not
ruined his hands for good. What a bed he prepared for those
old roses. Every inch of soil was removed for four feet.
That makes a hole deeper than it sounds till one stands in
it. Then the whole pit was floored with irregular chunks of
stone and filled with topsoil and manure. A good supply of
bonemeal and 5-10-5 was added for good measure, soaked
into the ground with the hose. We wanted to give these old-
timers a break.

This spring, when planted, they responded wonderfully.
One of these days the Harrison's Yellow, really a lovely rose
and very early, we'll move and put in another Rosa Mundi
with the Colonials. Best of it with such roses, they seem to
require little care. Blights and insects leave them largely
alone. The Old Scotch rose is the only one we've had trouble with so far.

Bill, in a digging mood that day, dug four more rose

holes, two on each side of the gate, filling them in the same way. Last fall we put four Blaze there to grow on the rails of the fence. They have blossomed so nicely this year that we are ready to put in four more this fall. Slowly does it.

In the garden nothing can be overlooked. Here and there along the new asparagus rows we noted blank spaces. Once frost had nipped the feathery plants and they were levelled, we realized no one could possibly tell next spring where the blank spaces were until it was too late to replant. So we drove stakes in now to remind us in March or early April where to do this. Fifty-five roots were needed. Far too many. Later we found that moles had been at the bed, attracted by grubs. We dosed the rows well with chlordane and cured that.

As with everything else, new growth needs care. Too often, however, it is the large and healthy plant that gets it, true to the old saw that they feed the fat pig at the fair.

ON THE 22ND OF AUGUST, at dawn, we went out with the Treweryn foot beagles, our fourteen and a half couples putting up two brace of hare in no time over at Bellevue. The countryside was unbelievable. It even tasted good, fall showing everywhere. In spite of the drought, sundrops, waxweed, white wood asters, tall snakeroot, masses of thoroughwort, blue lobelias, all the wildflowers were more than a match for our pampered chrysanthemums at home.

There the hollyhock seedlings, well watered right along, were almost ready for their transplanting. Enough corn was picked each day to serve our needs and give sufficient to freeze so that we were eating corn on the cob until the end of the next July. Squash was also stored in the deep freeze as it ripened, as were lima beans, bush limas, bush beans and okra. Long since we had laid in our peas. We found it useful as the limas podded to keep the vines well dusted with rotenone. It seemed incredible what that garden really was giving, but, oh, how we longed for rain!

It went to 98 degrees for three or four days as August ended. Garry lived for the brook. One day as he was larking about there, cool and contented, it made me envious so I walked in, clothes and all, just to enjoy a bit of the fun myself. I never saw a dog more astounded. Evidently, in his mind my place was on the bank where it had always been. Out he got and stood there staring, our positions reversed.

Why do ordinary clothes collect mud so when wet? I had to take a shower in them to get it off.

"The valleys also are covered ever with corn;
they shout for joy, they also sing!"

5

AUTUMN

GOING FOR THE PAPER this morning in the post-
box at the turn of the lane, I was reminded of the difficul-
ties of getting such things about in the old days. Our
county began pioneering with newspapers and pamphlets as
far back as the late 1700's. The first is generally regarded
as the *Gazette* which was published at the county seat once
a week. It is hard for us to picture the almost unsurmounta-
ble problem of distributing such a paper around the country.

What the editors did do was make use of an apprentice in
the printing office who could ride, providing him with a
horse, a set of ample saddlebags and a long tin horn, which
was hung around his neck by a cord. The bags were filled
with copies of the paper and off the lad went on a two-day
circuit up and down the township and county lanes, blowing
his horn at crossroad tavern, blacksmith shop or mill—

there were no stores as we understand them—even stopping at farmhouse doors if the people were on his list.

The newssheets were small, the earliest ones being only 10 by 16 inches, so two saddlebags could carry a lot. Local distribution was presumably made in turn from the bundles left by the apprentice at key points. One can imagine how these old papers were read and reread in the days when news travelled slowly and was valued the more. How the lad with his horn must have been welcomed. It is of record that part of the perquisites of his office consisted in pies and tarts and spring-cold cider given him by farmers' wives as he made his weekly rounds. Regular stopping places were arranged for the night, bed and board paid for by the editors. What a map of the county that boy must have carried in his head.

We even had a little paper of our own here at the Yellow Springs, a hundred years ago and more. It went by the odd name of *Literary Casket and General Intelligencer*. The printing office was in the old building built during the Revolution to serve as a hospital for the sick and wounded after Brandywine and during the encampment at Valley Forge. Washington Hall, it was—and still is—called, for it was erected at the General's order. *The Literary Casket and General Intelligencer* did not last very long, but it had the distinction of being non-political, in days when most publications were strictly partisan. But these are ancient things. Today, thanks to the Vails, the post comes on time and nobody needs a horn except when a registered letter arrives. Then Mr. Vail sounds a toot or so on a different sort of horn.

FEW THINGS CAN be quite so disheartening as drought. Anyone can endure heat, even wallow in humidity for a spell, but drought knows no half measures;

once it really strikes, it kills. Our second autumn gave us a
taste of that. The thermometer reached 100-101 degrees for
three days. No real rain had fallen since June. It is hot and
no mistake when the grackles fly with their nibs open, as
they did then. It was tragic to see the corn on the top
field grow brittle as it wilted, then died on the stalk. How
man has dreaded the days when water fails him. His cry
under the lash of it echoes through the ages.

"The hay is withered away, the grass faileth; there is no
green thing; Gladness is taken away and joy out of the
plentiful field."

The old words are still true. Gladness can be taken away
when green things die. Yet we ourselves were lucky. In spite
of the parching fields, our garden, on the slope, not far
from two springs, must have caught some moisture under-
ground, some saving dew from above, for it never let us
down that year till frost. Squash, tomatoes, lima beans,
string beans, okra were abundant. Only corn could not
mature without rain. We didn't pick a single nubbin from
our two last rows. Stalks never reached three feet. These
rows had been seeded late, it is true, but normal rains would
have saved them. We had plenty of corn, however, from
the earlier rows.

It was in September that the woodchucks really got to
work on what was left of the field corn. A skunk likes corn
and will take much of it if he can, but he does not usually
bend the stalks down as the woodchucks do to get at his ear.
The skunk's trick is to reach up as far as he can. We had
proof of that in the vegetable patch. He certainly reached
high there. The woodchuck—groundhog, if you like—eats
his ears where he gets them, leaving the gnawed cob. The
skunk rarely does so, preferring to stretch up, nip off an
ear to his taste, then carry it away to eat in peace and quiet
somewhere else.

We bolstered ourselves for a while with the hope that

Garry, now a year old and sleeping out o' nights, might discourage some of this looting, but scent of that sort does not seem to be his forte. He tries hard enough to unravel a rabbit's tortuous line, his long ears sweeping the ground, when he is lucky enough to spy one. Feather or leather, the old saying was. Which will meet across a springer's nose? Garry's ears are leather all right, and curly enough for anybody's taste, but rabbits are too sharp for him. We've never seen him more than sniff at a groundhog's earth. One skunk was enough—for him and for us. We all agreed on that.

If ever a dog was spoiled, Garry was, especially by Eugene who loved to have him leap up at him. He'd feed him on the sly at meals despite our forbidding him to do so.

"Don't you see he'll be big some day? People won't like it, being knocked off their pins. Or having him bother them begging at table."

"Garry no beeg! He iss poopy! He like play. Ich! I lof heem! I lof heem!"

The old man would bend over and let Garry chew at his ear. His must have been leather all right, for it seemed indestructible as he grumbled endearingly—I suppose in Ukrainian. In any case, Garry knew just what he said and slobbered bites and kisses galore. Eugene had the husbandman's gift, a passion for animals. They loved him in return. I'll wager he'd have done well with the swine if we'd had them. Alena, too, loved Garry and did her best to spoil him.

"Ah, Missus, Garry, he iss leetle boy. Ve mus' not hurt his feelink! I theenk hungry he iss now."

No wonder his ribs bulged.

As the drought held, we had to change plans for fall planting. It stayed too dry to plough for barley until it was too late for it. So we decided to wait for rain and then plough the upper west field and seed to wheat, which could go in later than the barley, using a grass mixture with it as before. Meanwhile, we watched the spring and kept the hose going on the terrace flowers and the beds where asters were blooming and chrysanthemums beginning to show a bit. Our periwinkle by the drive got a good soaking, too, every week. Vinca needs plenty of peat moss and water at the start. When it seemed safe to risk the spring, we still soaked the fruit saplings. Indeed, I think we saved them. The vegetable garden got little or no watering that year, but somehow our muskmelons ripened, small but sweet and filled with liquid. Where does it come from? They seemed to be growing in dust.

We did have a rain on the 5th of September, a thunder shower, not the slow three-day soaker we longed for. Still, it helped. The wild blue asters above the spring seemed the fresher for it. Bur marigold was all about now, especially in the low spots.

We were so cheered by the rain that we even arranged to get several tons of rich, screened topsoil and have a final try at remaking the lawn in front where damage left by the builders was still too much in evidence. How hard it is to have—and keep—a really satisfying lawn. Flowers are child's play compared to grass. Yet houses should grow from it naturally. Trees and shrubs are pleasant things we'd hate to do without, but grass one must have. It speaks to the heart.

THE EVENING WE HAD the thunderstorm, I was reading John Buchan's *Three Hostages*. In all his books, Lord Tweedsmuir makes houses come alive, but rarely does he catch the feel of one so satisfying as here.

There is an odour about a country house which I love better than any scent in the world—a mixture of lamp and dog and wood smoke—wood smoke, tobacco, the old walls and wafts of the country coming in at the windows. I liked it best in the morning when there was a touch in it of breakfast cooking.

We know those scents and love them as he did. Even while reading his words, we could catch the faint, yet pungent odour from the hearth where raindrops had found their way down the chimney to stir dead ashes to a reminder of old logs burning. Terrace borders, freshened by rain as they never really are by hosing, sent wafts of the country in to us, just as they had done for Buchan. Flowers, reviving mint, undertones from the oats stubble where our grass had begun to show, all were a part of our old house that evening, thanks to the benison of rain.

That little shower cleared the skies and brought a freshness almost as of fall to the breeze. On Labor Day we went to a small hunter show at the Corner. It was so cool sitting on the bank there that my wife went home for a jersey, the heat of two days ago forgotten. We spent the day at the show, letting the farm run itself for a spell, as it's perfectly able to do, while we met old friends, lunched on turkey sandwiches and watched young Jamie from Pigeon Run place with his hunter over the outside course. It was his first try. A good day and the farm none the worse for it, of course. Most worries are in the mind. Not so many things we fear really happen.

While we were gone, Eugene had a glorious crack at building a bridge above the barn, no one there to say him nay. We hadn't the very least need for it. The dry gully it covered was scarcely a foot deep and not wide, but bridge it he would. As always, he built for the ages. The bridge rests on beams 6 by 8 inches, of solid oak, so old and hard they'll turn a sixpenny nail. Eugene had found these beams somewhere in the barn.

"She stant—thees bridge. I theenk. She stant now."

We're sure of that. The bridge will outlast our house and barn together.

Taking advantage of another bit of rain, Horace came over and worked on the lawn in readiness for its new top-soil. When two loads came, 11 cubic yards of fine soil, we filled the new coldframe first, using the rest on the lawn.

In the garden a few late cauliflowers surprised us by ripening. The borders around the library terrace and the beds so close to them had been watered all summer without much trouble. They certainly repaid us now. Zinnia, hearts-ease, marigold, ageratum, petunia—popcorn seems the best for our low borders—begonia, maple-leaf begonia, bouvardia, impatiens, periwinkle, geranium, candytuft, sweet alyssum, *Sedum sieboldii,* pansies, even this late, centranthus, abelia, rose-of-Sharon, clematis, roses, mint, sweet marjoram, pennyroyal, tiger lilies, Loddon Gold, larkspur, spiderflower, calendula, morning-glories, scabiosa, gaillardia, aster, phlox, chrysanthemum, late poppies, late lemon lilies—it would be hard to name them all. I think that the old-fashioned rose-of-Sharon, white with just a faint blush of pink, we like the best. We can forgive its tendency to shed blossoms. Fresh ones are always coming on. They are so cool, tall-clustered, giving colour round the house when everything seems conquered by the heat. And how bees love them!

It really was miraculous the way that little terrace settled in. The old paving brick, mellowed by generations of use, helped, of course. So did the weathered stone of the ha-ha, but the flowers and the shrubs really did it. In making those borders, we had gone down two feet, refilling with good soil and manure. This was easy to do while the terrace was being made.

EARLY FALL BROUGHT US the night hawks soaring and gliding. At least, we noticed them more and heard the sound of their peent! peent! overhead. Each season has its own sounds naturally, just as it has its own scents. August dog-days till September are katydid and cricket time. Sheep across the lane seem restless when the nights are heavy. We hear them complaining about it. Days then are haunted by the plaintive notes of the mourning dove—he always seems far off.

IN MID-SEPTEMBER we took another break to see the Treweryn Beagles win the pack class over at the Rose Tree as well as the 13-inch class. Having run to this pack on foot after hare for almost thirty years, we naturally were pleased. Another thrill was that of seeing our kennel huntsman, Charlie Smith, win second place in the horn-blowing contest. It is a brave thing to hear the short hunting horn properly sounded in the notes of Move Off, Drawing Covert, Drawn Blank, the Find, Gone Away, Gone to Ground, the Kill, Come Away Home and the rest. These notes are traditional, coming to us, so they say, from the Conqueror's days. Not many can make a woodland ring as Charlie can, voice and horn, cheering hounds. One contestant blew the old-time curving cowhorn, deep-throated, soughing in note, reminding us of foxhounds on the Virginia hills. He blew it well.

Back home new chores were waiting. How they do crop up. Each season is going to be the easy one, with work well in hand. It never is. How dull, were it so. Now we gave what poison ivy we could find a farewell shot and kept on with our watering. "The ground is chapt, for there was no rain in the earth," says the Prophet Jeremiah. He should have seen our fields.

ON THE 25TH OF SEPTEMBER, we called it a year as far as some of the annuals went, and began to clear the upper border, mindful of bulbs soon to go in. Iris, though late for it, I suppose, and far too dry, was separated and replanted by the rear wall, where it has done well. Phlox also was divided where clumps had grown too large and replanted, some of it, under the kitchen windows. The troublesome long border by the asparagus bed was removed entirely at this time. We have told already how we had curtailed it, but now we were glad to see it go.

Next day, anniversary of the Argonne, much more peaceful and satisfying work was done here at Melbrook. Eight multiflora roses were dug from the borders, where they had been temporarily planted. We reset them along the lane above the barn. Lima-bean vines and bush limas were pulled up and burned. We wrestled and tugged with Eugene's deep-rooted bean poles, crowbar and spade to help us pry them up. Drought-harried cucumber vines were also raked up and burned. The young hollyhocks, a row of them, were watered. They were doing nicely, almost ready for transplanting now. A final scything was given below the springhouse where pokeweed had grown tall.

TO US, IN OUR LITTLE VALLEY, frost comes early. We had learned that our first year here. It is disheartening to see flowers cut down and late vegetables blackened before October has hardly begun, then to see weeks of warm and mellow weather lasting on beyond Indian summer, almost in mockery of the first destructive frost. To offset this, once we had learned our lesson, we made sure that plenty of chrysanthemums were in the terrace borders and the nearby beds by the end of September at the latest. They could stand a lot of cold and not be in the least affected by first frosts. In the garden we could not do very much, but one old-fashioned trick stood us in good stead. My wife, alert to such things, pulled a dozen or so of the tomato plants up by the roots and hung them upside down from the side beams of the haymows in the barn. These plants were green and healthy, filled heavily with unripened fruit. All ripe tomatoes had been removed. Hanging there in the barn, secure from frost, the plants withered slowly, but the green fruit ripened. Well into November, six weeks after the garden tomatoes had gone for good, we were gathering quantities of delicious ripe tomatoes from the strung-up plants in the barn. It was little trouble to take the plants indoors, but surely more than worth the effort.

GARRY WAS A RARE LAD at helping in all this. Whatever we did, he must have a share in it, usually managing to carry what we had raked carefully in one place to a pile or several piles of his own choosing somewhere else. Naturally this can prove infuriating. I'd tear off my belt to flay his hide, but never quite got around to it as he rolled over on his back or stood there, red haws showing below his wistful eyes, really not in the least repentant, but reading me like a book. Eugene, too, could read me.

"Ach! Ach! You lof' heem! You not hit heem! I see eet! You lof' heem!"

In the end Garry would lark about in a rigadoon of his own, bite the old man's ear and scatter more of our rakings. He was the boy for *joie de vivre*, knowing how well he owned the two of us.

One thing I always wanted to ask Eugene, but the language bar prevented. What numbskulls he must have thought us. We hadn't a word of Ukrainian. There is a lot of woody nightshade growing by the wall on the hill. Poisonous, but a beautiful flower. Old people say that it is the best safeguard known against the bewitching of hogs. I wonder if it grows in the Ukraine. Or if Eugene and his father made use of it with their twenty swine? There is a prodigious science of plants and the powers of evil. Old herbals are full of it, fascinating reading, but word of mouth is better still. How these saws, wise or otherwise, have held through the ages. Only last week we were asked why we had no sunflowers planted on the south side of the house to ward off fever. Why not?

GARRY IS A GREAT INVESTIGATOR of everything that blossoms, wild or no. Also, he is a creature of habit. Regularly each summer evening he makes his rounds of the terrace, having a sniff at each flower, never stepping over the edging but stretching his neck for its perfume. We should have called him Ferdinand.

Critically minded friends scoff at his aesthetic sense and say that he is simply smelling out toads, drawn there by the watering. He did find one a year ago, but the toad in ways unknown got the better of the contest. Perhaps Garry feared he was giving him warts.

We have never known two such slaves of habit as Garry and Eugene. Indeed, they are alike in most ways, each liking to follow his own bent. In winter Garry sleeps in his house by the kitchen door. In summer his basket is on the front terrace where the stone flags are cooler. Will he go out the front door to reach it? Assuredly not. When the door is being locked for the night, he stands there inside, looking out at his bed a few feet away. Then he marches back through the house to the kitchen and so out by the back door, rolling over there for a good-night scratch on his belly. Only then does he trudge all the way around the house to his bed in front. Nothing can change this routine. Like Eugene, I suppose, it always has been that way.

IN OCTOBER, Alena and Eugene left us, missing, we think, the Ukrainian colony in town. We hated to see them go. Eugene, loving the land—still hopeful of swine—wanted to stay. Alena, a gay, birdlike little creature for all her years and her kerchief, loved to talk. She just had to be with people. We did what we could to find work for them in the city where they are among their own people and seem happy. Now and then they write us a line to ask about Garry. He was their hearts' delight.

Somehow, even without Eugene's disapproving shrugs, work went on at Melbrook. Three clematis were planted where they could grow on trellises against the library walls —Mrs. Cholmondeley, Contesse de Bouchaud and Duchess of Edinburgh. The first has done the best, giving us most lovely clear blue flowers this year. The others are growing more slowly and have not blossomed. Clematis is temperamental and full of queer quirks, liking cool feet, a touch of sun above and just the right amount of lime in the soil.

We have found that the tender part is the first six or eight inches above the ground. It helps to put an inverted flower pot over this, passing the stem through the hole in the bottom of the pot. Later, when the vine is tougher, the pot can be broken and removed. Care must be taken in watering, however, to make sure that the pot does not keep water away from the roots. It can do this if its rim sinks too deeply in the ground.

A GARDEN CHORE about this time was digging a pit to bury our carrots in. Ensconced there under a blanket of leaves, they supplied us well through the winter. This always reminded me of the great earth-covered mounds of Baden after the war, where field beets were stored as cattle forage. They were immensely big—mangel-wurzels actually—yet some of them surprisingly sweet as we'd slice a bit off with a trench knife and gnaw it.

IT PAYS, WHEN POSSIBLE, to put things away ready for use, but too often we postpone the sharpening and oiling and cleaning that save time later. This fall, however, we did manage to saw off the lima-bean poles to more useful length. Even buried as deeply as Eugene had set their butts, bless his heart, they were far too tall. No one could pick top beans without a ladder. Naturally, none of us fetched a ladder. Over 18 inches were cut off and that problem solved for this year.

There was much to do this fall readying up, raking the garden and burning what we raked. Lots of manure went on later. Unquestionably vegetable stalks make fine compost, but so many pests are about these days that we feel it wise to burn most garden refuse. Perhaps we are wasteful in this, for we swear by compost. Each year we wonder— to burn or not to burn. We did give our cornstalks to neighbours at Pippin Hill for fodder. While working in the garden we found a chance to dig a trench in front of the barn and fill it with good earth and manure for the hollyhocks. They would be transplanted there a little later.

ONE OF THE MOST FAITHFUL workers all winter was John who came over from Wallingford on many a Saturday to help us. Nothing could tire him; nothing dim the flash of his smile as he pitched in. Almost a year had passed since he had helped Frank and the others put in the pine and spruce-tree saplings. With Eugene gone, we found it necessary to get more help from these fine lads from time to time. We could count on John.

Our first task this October was cutting back phlox and moving some of it. Coloured phlox, not magenta, but a really good pink and white reminding one of mountain laurel, was put in by the spring. A good deal of the old blue iris was also transplanted to the side of the spring-house. Heliopsis was planted in some of the borders—*Scabra gigantea*. Dutch iris was divided between the lower and middle borders. Everything moved was given a real soaking. Everything already in the beds or recently planted was marked with a small stick-label. We knew their where-abouts by heart now in fall, but next spring with nothing showing above ground would be a different matter.

EARLY IN THE MONTH we began our first try here with wildflowers, choosing a spot well shaded by trees and an immense old clump of lilacs just around the corner from the terrace. Economy of effort had led us to concentrate all our flowers in that immediate area. After all, we wanted to enjoy them not be slaves to them. We fertilized heavily and used much peat moss and leaf mould, then had planted there 12 wakerobins, *Trillium erectum*; 24 *Trillium grandiflorum*; 24 foam-flowers, *Tiarella cordifolia*; 3 yellow lady's-slippers, 12 Jack-in-the pulpits, 24 Dutchman's-breeches; 24 galax, 24 Canada violets, 24 bugleweed, ajuga; 12 bleeding hearts, *Dicentra eximia*; 12 bishop's-hats, *Epimedium roseum*; 12 lungworts, pulmonaria; 12 pipsissewa, 12 wild lilies-of-the-valley; 10 astilbe, 36 Virginia bluebells, mertensia; 6 Christmas roses; 50 Christmas ferns; 24 wood ferns, 24 cinnamon ferns; 50 maidenhair ferns; 2 wild white azaleas, 2 pinxterflowers, 2 Oregon grape—*Mahonia*.

A light rain during the planting was a blessing indeed. We also had time to put in a trumpet creeper by the corner of the barn—a long day's work, but a happy one.

FIRST HEAVY FROST came on the 8th. Horace seeded the front lawn, using a good deal of manure and 5-10-5 worked in. We had kept a record of flowers noted here during our first year, wild ones, those cultivated, shrubs, trees, everything that blossomed, large or small. They came to 154. This year, by the end of July, our score is 188. We'll easily reach 200. As far as wildflowers go, it is largely a matter of opening one's eyes.

MORE AND MORE PLANTING went on after frost. In the green bed, so called, we put one Franklin tree, 2 mountain laurel and 3 azaleas—Ledifolia alba, white, schlippenbachi, flesh-coloured, and altaclarense, yellow. The hollyhock seedlings, sturdy plants by now, were moved to in front of the barn, thanks again to John. A few new peonies were put in the upper border. Some White Admiral phlox was used to reinforce the middle and lower borders. We seem to like it as much as our old favourite Miss Lingard. My wife, busier than ever, potted the last of the frost-nipped geraniums and begonias and fetched them round in fine shape indoors. She has green fingers as well as thumbs. This was our first chance to use the wide sills we had made in the library bay. Outside late endive and parsley were seeded in the coldframe. This should have been done six weeks earlier, but some things just have to wait.

MEANWHILE, Noel was busy with the fields. We could plough now, thanks to the rain. He began by turning over the upper west field with his great disk-plough—but too fast. It is his greatest fault. I think he is driving a tank into battle in his mind's eye. Furrows flow out like the bow wave of a clipper with a bone in her teeth. But plough he did and harrow too, disking slowly, for a change, and well. After liming, we seeded the field to Pennoll wheat with a grass mixture for sod—timothy and brome-grass. It was too late in the year for alfalfa, as we should have liked. For fertilizer we used, in the same amounts per acre as before, 5-10-5 and borax.

As I watched the ploughing, I could not help but think of the changes that have taken place since the old days. Once these very same fields must have been tilled, probably by oxen, drawing the great wooden plough that was commonplace then. Such ploughs were over ten feet long, immensely heavy—that is why oxen were used to drag them. At first even their coulters and mouldboards were of wood. Later they were shod with iron for three feet in front, a boon in breaking new ground, where roots would sometimes tear the coulter from the beam or a hidden rock—we've plenty here—break it to slivers. How can we picture the labour of it all?

I looked again at the boy sitting carefree on his tractor. The beam of an old plough was low and naturally tended to choke easily on grass or stubble or even on manure being turned under. A boy of Noel's age or a good deal younger usually had the task of trudging beside each furrow as the ploughman turned it, so as to clear the beam and the share whenever they fouled. A far cry this from Noel's disk-plough. I wonder if he can realize what farming meant in his great-grandfather's day. Yet that old wooden plough was the very symbol of survival here. Not for nothing was the representation of just such a plough made the most prominent part of our county's seal way back in 1683.

How much man owes to the plough, yet never dreams of it. An acre, for instance, was once the amount of land a man could plough in one day with two oxen. A furlong was the length of one furrow ploughed by two oxen without pause for a breather. A rod, now 16½ feet, was originally the length of the ox-goad, long enough to reach from the plough hales to the lead ox. It was used to lay off the distance between the first furrow in one direction and the return furrow, back towards the starting point, before the strip was ploughed between the two furrows. Hence our rod or pole as a unit of measure.

I should have been about my work, as the boy was, but it was hard to break the spell of old memories handed down to us in this long-settled land. During the Revolutionary War, people here relied mostly on rye for their bread because they knew that rye would do better on poor land than wheat. They didn't relish the rye, but they stuck manfully to it, putting winning the war first. Old letters are revealing.

"Sooner would I eat rye bread to my dying day than meanly surrender my liberty and sell posterity," wrote a Nantmeal farmer as he went off to the war. I could see the hills where he had lived from the slope we were ploughing at Melbrook. Not to sell posterity? How strange that sounds in our ears. I wonder how the Welfare State would deal with one so obstinate as to have posterity in mind as well as his own immediate needs? We could do with more of his kidney today. We've come quite a way, down the years, from that point of view, to our combines and tractors. Yet I wonder? I wonder?

Noel had a good seed-drill, but he was not mindful of saving soil one day in October when he ran his wheat rows straight up and down the hill. Such slips are the exception nowadays when most people seem soil-conscious and well aware of conservation usage.

Next day it rained. Then it rained all night and it rained next morning—a slow, soft, sinking-in rain. What sound in all the world is quite so sweet, so reassuring to the ear, as rain on roof when land is parching? When it cleared, we put 2 tons of manure and 80 pounds of 5-10-10 on the old asparagus bed. For a year now it had been our pampered darling. People made a great joke of it, saying we had gone stark mad, yet the fruition paid off handsomely and to spare. We had worked so hard our first year here, tearing out those horrible weeds, an inch or so at a time, little by little uncovering what could not even be seen before, that we were determined now to get the most from it. So feed the old bed we did, and feed it again, until like Garry with Eugene, it must have been bursting.

It is surprising how much planting goes on in the fall. In some ways, there is more of it than in the spring. Everyone thinks of bulbs, the daffodils and the rest, but that is not the half of it. Nearly all dormant stock can go in then from large trees to shrubs. The day after we had the rain, for example, we planted 3 Concord and 3 Portland grapevines on the little trellises we had made for them on the sunny slope above the barn. Grapes attract a lot of Japanese beetles, it is true. In spite of bagging the fruit, marauding birds, especially blackbirds, will soon learn the trick of pecking through the paper when the grapes are ripe. Yet for all this, who can resist a ripe bunch of grapes in the fall? Looted or not, a good many manage to survive.

Now and then new plantings arrive, wrapped in burlap, the folds held fast with old nails by way of pins. That surely reminds us of the days when things were more simply handled. It was time now also for getting in bulbs and the long, slow rain had made conditions ideal for it. My wife and I planted some liles in the borders. Near the wildflowers, we scattered *Anemone fulgens, Anemone blanda atrocoerulea,* chionodoxa—glory-of-the-snow; grape-hyacinth; Loddon lilies, snowflakes; wolfbane; Candlemas bells and snow crocus. We tried seeding sweet alyssum along the edge of the ha-ha wall, but nothing came of it. Month by month, we have our setbacks, almost as many of them as our lucky breaks. They are worth it, for how else could we learn?

WHEN WE HAD PUT AWAY the garden hose, turned off the outside taps and lugged porch chairs to the barn, we knew it meant goodbye to Indian summer. Incidentally, we were careful to drain all our hose thoroughly. If this be not done, it is the easiest thing in the world to have the hose freeze in winter sharp spells and thus be ruined. Main chore now, however, was the raking and saving of leaves. The Dobson brothers turned up in force to help and left us spick-and-span till more leaves fell. It was good, though, to see the compost pits overflowing.

Sudden snow came on November 7th, playing hob with the cowpeas. Once they are flattened, a combine can make little headway with them. Next day the brook across the lane was frozen. Far too early, although the cold did not last. That first snow was deep, however, far deeper than we had thought, drifting badly over our drive until we were snowed in for fair. Again the Dobsons saved us, George and Bob and Gerrit getting over the blocked roads somehow to dig us out. In trouble, summer or winter, we turn to them.

A week later, snow gone, John and I planted some early tulips, jonquils, campernelles and daffodils. These were in the terrace border. By the front of the house we put in Dutch iris and more daffodils. Blue scillas were already in. Over near the barn we scattered, then dug in a good many more daffodils and iris. Below the springhouse towards the road, we planted Golden Harvest and King Alfred daffodils. The last-named, by our reckoning, are not the best sort for a natural setting, tending to grow a bit tall and break.

We worked hard all day at the bulbs, John and I, well soaked by mist and slush, but we got everything in that we had planned. John is indefatigable regardless of weather. Whatsoever his hand findeth to do, he surely does it with his might if anyone does.

OUR CUTBACK BANK, where the drive had been widened, still showed raw in spite of the euonymus we had tried there, so now in mid-November we put in 30 Max Graf roses at a venture. Not one died. The bank is steep. Why they have not eroded or washed out completely, we don't know. This year we have ordered 30 more Max Graf to form a second row. The first lot blossomed surprisingly well. A few other roses where the pitch of the bank is not so steep have done wonders really in this year's drought, blooming on, a few at a time, all summer.

REAL LOSS CAME to us that autumn when Ikie, our mouser, died, victim of a plague that swept our valley. Three cats went in one day at Pippin Hill. We spoke to our neighbours and found the same thing true on their farms. I suppose a distemper of some sort was to blame, but it must have been virulent. We still miss Ikie. He played some havoc among the birds, no doubt, but he also ridded house and barn of mice for us. Moles minded their business when he was around. We saw no rats at all. Rabbits kept clear of the garden patch. Best of all, he and Garry made friends in the end. Garry, always a rough-and-tumble chap, assumed that he was to take charge, but Ikie's claws, razored neatly once or twice across his nose, soon taught him respect for his betters. It was not long before they curled up together, Ikie sleeping between Garry's paws. Poor Ikie! He disappeared one day to die hidden away by himself. We never found a trace of him. These things hurt. Every farm needs a cat or so to control mice and rats and moles as well. Ikie was particularly strong on moles.

AFTER THE SNOW we cut back old and new asparagus beds, raked up the stalks, then manured the new bed well. The old one had had its share. There seemed to be no end to our planting in November. One Saturday a boy came over to help with new roses. We have tried planting them in spring and fall. On the whole, fall has given us better results. Perhaps the mild winters we've had have helped. It seems likely, however, that the root stocks, though dormant in fall, have not yet dried out quite so thoroughly. Very early in spring the tiny threads of the rootlets are already working through the soil; whereas spring-planted stock would not be in the ground yet. In any case, we favour fall planting of roses whenever we can get them.

Craig and I began work early and kept at it late, digging the necessary holes, fertilizing, putting in, by dark, 4 Blaze roses along the post-and-rail fence at the gate, 2 more Blaze by the side door of the barn, 1 Temptation by the garage wall, 2 Dream Girl by the kitchen wall, 1 Peach Glow, and lovely it is, by the library wall where its trellis was already in place. We then got to work at the bed made ready long ago for the Colonials, putting in 4 out of the 7 we had chosen: Old Moss Pink, Rosa Mundi, Damascus and Old Scotch. The other three were not sent us till spring. Perhaps they are not suitable for fall planting. Twelve more roses went in on the bank near the door of the house. These were Carpet of Gold, Inspiration and Dream Girl.

We took a lot of pains with these roses, digging each hole

wide as well as deep, dropping a stone or two at the bottom, then sand and topsoil, half and half, then more topsoil, manure and rose food, mixed. Finally topsoil alone, well tamped. We earthed up the stocks some 5 or 6 inches with more earth and peat moss against winter frost.

By the sundial borders we put in a butterfly bush, Ile de France. It must be listed among our failures. We have grown these shrubs often as easily as weeds, but here two have failed already. One was planted in the fall; the other in spring. A great walnut tree grows nearby. Perhaps that is the reason. A friend of ours who runs a successful orchard near us says that a walnut tree will kill any apple sapling planted within fifteen yards of it. Oddly, he thinks that peach saplings are not so easily affected. We'll soon see, for we have both apple, peach and did have the butterfly bush, near our walnut.

THIS NOVEMBER DAY was one of the busiest we had all fall. While Craig and I were at the roses, Bob, Gerrit and John Dobson, all the team except Kenny, came over to carry load after load of firewood in wheelbarrows from the barn to the terrace, where they stacked it neatly and covered the pile with a tarpaulin. It was handy to have dry logs just outside the library door all winter. Inside we have a huge copper kettle beside the hearth holding half a dozen logs and kindling.

How infinite are the little jobs, yet they weave for us the pattern of our daily lives. They are not trivial. The whole place hummed that day, everyone busy as nailers. On the hill Noel and Bill and Clarence were combining what they could of the cowpeas in the lower and middle east fields. I never saw a finer stand of them or one more thickly set with pods—till the early snow flattened so many.

It was heartbreaking, for Noel had worked hard there. It and the corn were his private venture.

LATER THAT AFTERNOON, when Craig and I had finished with the roses and spread 1½ tons of manure on the vegetable garden, Noel disk-ploughed it under for us. When he had drilled in our wheat, timothy and brome-grass a fortnight earlier, quite a lot of seed was left over, although we had given him just what should have gone in. To save this, we had the Dobsons broadcast it for us in the old-fashioned way, hoping that some of it at least might be helped by fall rains to take hold among the drilled wheat. It did. In spring when the wheat was harvested, our friend from Uwchlan on the combine, a good neighbour helping us out, asked if a blind man had done the planting.

"I can see the regular rows all right. What I mean. But there's wheat every which way. I can't make it out. What I mean."

No wonder. That broadcasting produced a maze. But it gave us a bit more grain for the mill and straw for Jamie's hunter.

Though late, our terrace flowers still showed a touch of bloom, violets and heartsease mostly. Under the lilacs, Christmas roses were opening. Snow crocus peeped beside the great rock. On the bank above the roses, violets were thick, all the richer for the dull November skies.

Thanksgiving Day, after church, we raked leaves thickly on the wildflower bed. It likes such a blanket. Then we made one of our saddest mistakes, seeding annual larkspur, well thinned with sand, in the borders. We also tried some delphinium. It seemed too late in the year for such seeding, but we went on with it anyway. Whatever the fault, not a single one of them showed in the spring.

How dull life would be if we were always right. The

surprises that come, the wonder that is always new, these are the things that make the game worthwhile. In his *Circle of the Seasons,* Edwin May Teale has caught for us this feeling:

What a natural wellspring, cooling and refreshing the years— is the gift of wonder! It removes the dryness from life and keeps our days fresh and expanding.

"For he saith to the snow, Be thou on the earth; likewise to the small rain and to the great rain of his strength."

6

SWEET THUNDER

WE TOOK ADVANTAGE of a lull in the weather to see our snow crocuses blooming, though it was still November. Then we seeded the lower half of our vegetable patch with rye, to be ploughed under in spring. We knew that this should have been done by mid-October at the latest, to give winter cover a chance to grow. Then, in spring, there would have been a thick mat of green to turn under. Few things loosen up heavy clays or tight soils better than this. As it was, our rye did not do too badly, for we were able to plough in a good deal of mulch in March.

Parts of the garden not sown to rye were covered with a thick layer of Eugene's summer-scythed grass, now well dried. It, too, served as excellent ground cover, preventing both erosion and the constant thaw and freeze that abet washout and leaching. Our garden being on a slope, we had to take precautions against such things. Horace helped us. It took little time, probably an hour to spread the dried grass; a little longer to broadcast and rake in the rye; but the gain in soil conditioning next spring, the ease in plough-ing and the harvest of vegetables we are garnering now are hard to believe.

GOOD OLD EUGENE. How we do miss him and Alena. I thought of him every time I passed the grass-mulched truck patch last winter or saw his old red cap still hanging where he had left it on a peg in the workshop. Before he went away, he tapped his beloved scythe blade to a scimitar's edge, oiled and greased it, then wrapped it tenderly in swaddling bands before he hung it up, like Old Black Joe's hoe. I think Eugene always hoped that he might be able to persuade Alena to come back. And then, who knows, maybe swine in the barn-house!

We shall never forget the arguments we had with both of them over fish. What an odd object of dispute it seems. Always they said they wanted some. My good wife tried every kind of fish in the market—halibut, sole, cod, what-ever she could buy. They seemed all right to us, but Eugene would look at them aghast, then shake his head. He was more finicky than Alena or more argumentative.

"Nock! Nock, Missus! Thees feesh eet iss not good. Eet iss not feesh from river!"

"Indeed, it's not," my wife would bridle. "I mean indeed it is. I mean it's fresh right from the sea. There couldn't be fresher."

"Och, ja! Missus! From sea. I say eet iss! Dirty feesh from sea. In Ukraine, good feesh he iss from river. He iss carp!"

We have tried them with fresh-run shad in season, ex-plaining that here at last was a river fish, freshly netted.

"Tcht! Tcht! I do not theenk eet, Missus. Thees iss beeg feesh. River feesh he iss beeg. But river feesh he iss carp. Always he iss carp."

It was useless. Love them as we did, we could not bring the Ukraine to Chester County. I will say Eugene was not easily defeated. He had hopes even of the brook across the lane.

"Thees iss little river. In river leetle feesh, I theenk. Good feesh! Trouts they are. First I make svine-house in barn-house. Ya! Then maybe ve get feesh! From river!"

Trout they were not, and he never got round to trying for them, but he kept in good heart. No wonder we have missed him and his wife. Their whimsies irked at times, but surely were forgivable. They never gave up. Both Alena and Eugene were tories to the heart. Everyone that came on the place was quietly appraised and given his or her social rating. Nothing was said of this, but the sorting and sifting were obvious. Before long, Garry, too, was turning into a first-class snob under Eugene's impeccable tutelage.

"Ugh! You bark at heem!"

We tried in vain to explain that Paul, our huckster, must come with the meat. All sorts of things must be delivered. It did no good. Whenever we were not looking, Eugene went on with his lessons. He taught with verve. We really pitied the man who took away unburnable trash, for he got the worst of it all. Eugene, strangely for a foreigner, was colour-conscious to a degree.

"Black man, he come! Garry! Queek! You see heem? Ugh!"

IN THE END, we had trouble as the delivery men grew restive. Garry loved to leap and bark, but he harboured no leaven of malice or wickedness in his young bones. The only thing he wanted to chew was Eugene's long-suffering ear and that was to show how he loved him. To calm their fears, however, the various drivers were given small rubber squirters by my wife. These are filled with water and some vinegar. It's a droll sight if ever was one to watch a six-foot man, armed with one of these squirters, designed I believe for an infant's more intimate needs, walking delicately like Agag up the drive, a small springer gambolling delightedly about him.

Garry's snobbery has finesse, we are sorry to say. He loves to pick up a special wastebasket of his own and carry it round indoors, offering it solemnly to everyone as if it were the alms basin at church. When, however, he decides that a person rates belowstairs, as the saying used to go, he passes them by, never, except for Alena and Eugene, offering his basket to anyone in the kitchen or from it. Thus is youth corrupted and democracy betrayed. But the year moved on, always something waiting, Garry or no.

It was after Thanksgiving when John and I gave the periwinkle by the drive a good coat of peat moss. The trumpet creeper was banked up with manure at the same time. Then we got to work burning the great piles of garden trash that had collected during the fall. The cedar slats or crosspieces of the grape trellises were painted green to preserve them. The little chores about a place like this never end. What goads and gadflies they can be till seen to.

THE FIRST DAY OF DECEMBER the bulldozer came over from Exton and rooted out two of our hedgerows in no time, thus giving us a fine ten-acre field in lieu of three small ones. It is fascinating to climb the hill at Melbrook now and visualize the changes that must have come to the slopes of this small croft since first men began to clear the trees and farm it. Too often we take our countryside for granted, overlooking the infinite labour that has transformed it so slowly through the centuries to what we know. Yes, and the infinite hopes and longings and heart-aches as well that have gone to shape the land. Many gen-erations have had a hand in it, not just our bulldozer.

Once all this country was wooded, of course, but oddly enough there was little brush below the forest trees. Indians saw to that, burning off saplings intermittently so that the trees stood in a gladelike fashion, grass beneath them. This facilitated the hunting of deer. When the first English and Welsh settlers came to such parkland, they "deaded" the trees by ringing them. This let in light at once for there were no more leaves. Wheat was then hoed in by hand, seeded in the rich forest soil, the trees still standing. Later, the little crop harvested by sickle, men cut down what trees they could and burned them. Still later, stumps were burned or dragged out by the roots by yokes of patient oxen or left to rot. It must have taken a hundred years before open pasture and plough and ley appeared as we see them on our hills today. It is good now and then to remember some of this.

While the tree felling was going on, it is hard to imagine how slowly a few perches were cleared about the cabins, year by year, a few acres at a time when the field-stone farmsteads came and the great barns rose as crops increased.

Indians hereabouts were kindly, giving the first settlers bear meat and venison to tide them over the early winters; wildfowl and eggs in summer. This helped a lot, but the donors were not always treated kindly in return.

IT IS SURPRISING how soon livestock was brought from overseas. Goats, hogs and chickens came first, hardy breeds standing the long voyage well. Horses, a few at least, came next. It's easier to ride than to walk. And then the cattle. These were not much to boast of, we are told. Finally sheep arrived.

It is difficult for us to picture this as we look at the great herds of Jersey and Guernsey milkers, the Black Angus and Hereford beefers, that graze the slopes nowadays or stand chewing their cuds in the peace of the water meadows.

Long ago, there being few fences, stock ranged at will, browsing at the clearings' edges. Brands and ear clipping served to identify them, something we are likely to associate with the West many generations later. Even in 1684 such marks were registered by law in the court records here. Soon, however, the inevitable interbreeding reduced such cattle as there were to culls. A county official, called the Ranger, was appointed back in 1724 whose duty it was to see that no bulls or stallions were at large. If found, these were put in pound and their owners fined heavily. Cows and mares and geldings were still allowed to graze where they pleased, but it was not long until the snake fences began to appear and stock could be kept in bounds. Cowbells, of course, were a necessity. They still are. I can hear one now as I write, sounding in the wooded strip across the stream where the alders grow, just as such bells have sounded for hundreds of years. In some ways, there have been surprisingly few changes. After all, the land itself is eternal, seedtime and harvest, whether man ruins it temporarily or not. There's comfort in that.

THE SOUND OF THE COWBELL carries me back to the hidden uplands, the little lost alps of Tyrol, where cattle graze close to the snow line and the sweet short turf lies open to the skies. They love their cattle there and the bells sound softly all the day. Here at home we love the cattle, too, for this is grazing land.

ONLY A WEEK AGO, Bill from the Corner, who has been helping me on the farm this summer, won first prize at Kimberton Fair judging beef stock. Not bad, that, for a lad who had just reached fifteen the week before. We are proud of Bill. He loves horses, too, taking care of four of them for his neighbours. On the farm when he starts a job, he finishes it and sweeps up the scraps, as it were. Not once have we seen him leave something half done. Not once has he neglected to put the axe or whatever he has been using back where it belongs. That's a trait we've seen little of. It will carry him far. When he won the livestock judging prize, my wife and I were as pleased as he was. It's no small beer to judge stock wisely in a crowd.

ONCE WE HAD PUT the beds and borders to sleep, there was little more we could do for them until spring, except to cover them and the wildflower bed also with a counterpane of leaves. Before we put the leaves on the wildflowers, we scattered a second bale of peat moss on for good measure. It seemed touch and go for a while whether we had smothered everything, but apparently not, for the flowers worked their way through the leaves handily enough when their time had come in spring. Leaves were also put on the asparagus beds as ground cover. In all our winter mulching, we tried to wait until the ground was reasonably hard with frost before covering it. The purpose of winter mulch is to keep cold in and heat out, we must remember, something we often forget in our haste to cover too early.

Before we mulched the green border, we seeded some poppies there as an experiment. Iceland poppies, Shirleys and orientals among them. The results in early summer were far more rewarding than we had expected, the brilliant colour of the poppies livening up the green border just when the azaleas and mountain laurels had ceased blooming.

SIXTEEN TONS of good cow manure, well rotted, went on the vegetable garden and the borders that fall. Shrubs, fruit saplings, boxwood, roses, hollyhocks, all got their share. We were fortunate in being able to get what manure we needed at reasonable cost. It seemed a lot in tonnage, none of this for the fields, but we begrudged not a pound of it, for we were starting from scratch, if anybody ever did, and had to build up organic content long robbed from the soil.

IN SPITE OF LEAVES and peat moss perhaps spread too generously about them, our first Christmas roses opened on the 6th of December to keep the snow crocuses company. How a Christmas rose speaks to the heart. No other flower in all the year is quite so welcome. It seems to reassure us that spring is on the way, even before real winter has begun. We watch for them eagerly, yet with reverence, too, for surely they carry a promise.

FOR A CHANGE from spreading manure and raking leaves and gathering fallen limbs and wind-torn branches for burning, we made a point now and then of leaving the farm and its cares to its own devices, as we drove to a meet of the foxhounds. There are two recognized packs within a few miles of us, and usually one of them crosses our fields every week. We love to see them, as they do no harm to the fields, the riders skirting wheat and showing some consideration for seeded ground by sticking to the headlands. Where hounds go we do not care, such a joy it is to see and hear them. As for the fox, the land is his quite as much as it is ours. His family tree goes back a long way in these hills. He has a right of way. Then, too, the hunt are our neighbours.

Although I have been hunting, off and on, for almost fifty years, my wife can spot a fox before I do every time as he breaks covert or glides slyly down a hedgerow unnoticed by the pack. She and Casper are the experts of the car brigade, but I must admit no one living can throw tongue like Casper when he shrieks his View-halloa. It's worth a cold day on the hills to hear him. He screams from the soles of his feet, if you know what I mean.

Now and then a hunt breakfast is given. The field are famished naturally after a day in the saddle, but steak-and-kidney pie or a great oyster pasty soon cures that.

Tradition says that Washington rode to hounds on these hills. I have no doubt that he did. Wayne of Waynesborough across the valley was devoted to the sport. Both would approve could they see the scarlet coats still with us and hounds still true to line.

TURKEY AND TREE were on hand for Christmas. This time we had a real tree, feeling that Garry was old enough to eschew mischief in that quarter. He really behaved well, apart from purloining a fallen crystal or two and eating them with relish and dispatch. What goes on inside that dog we'd like to know. So far nothing has disagreed and nothing includes a lot.

In addition to the turkey and the tree, I decided I'd pick up a pair of wooden stable buckets. That shouldn't take me long. I little knew. Here and there about the county I drove, like Eugene growing more and more determined to find what I wanted as the chances of getting it lessened. A simple wooden pail? What for? What would I want a bucket for—watering a horse? Or feeding? Finally I found them, the two I needed, but I had to go all the way to Morgantown in Lancaster to get them. The Pennsylvania Dutch thereabouts are not easily inveigled into changing their ways amid the sundry and manifold changes about them. I sensed that they might hold to wooden buckets just as I do. They did. I was as proud of running these buckets to ground as ever Eugene was of his Austrian scythe.

As I was busy painting them next day, the old man who had bulldozed our hedges sent his wife and grandson over to ask if they might cut a juniper for their Christmas tree. Naturally we were glad to give them their pick. A good many people nearby get their trees here, but not one has been cut without permission being asked. We are grateful for that. And lucky, too, for in some places theft and destruction of any sort of evergreen trees at Christmas are distressing. A home-grown juniper—we always call them cedars—may lack the aroma of the balsam and it may not be quite so easy to trim, but it is the Christmas tree of the country here and always has been.

Christmas Eve, Garry and I walked on the hills, glad to stretch our legs a bit and glad to see so many juncos and cardinals and tree sparrows about. We used to call the juncos snowbirds. How they love to foregather with the tree sparrows, feeding along the edges of the wood or by old fencerows and hedges. Here at Melbrook three spruce trees near the barn seem their favourite haunt in winter. Nothing could be more cheery than their chatter. On our way home Garry and I wassailed the apple trees for old times' sake. The one by the drive proved grateful. Such piles upon piles of fruit as we've gathered this summer would be hard to imagine.

SEEING SO MANY BIRDS about at Christmas made me think how odd it is that people ask us how we stand the country in winter—it must be so empty. That is one thing it is not. Actually, it is filled to the brim with life and

each day different. We see far more in winter than in summer really when leaves and vegetation screen the clutches
of the birds, the nests, or so-called stabs of the rabbits, the
setts or forms of the hare—all the house keeping arrangements of pelt and wing. A few of our friends den up in
winter as the groundhog does, but we are far more in touch
with the others.

Take birds, for example. Apart from their songs, they
are more in evidence when trees are bare than ever they
are in June. Their variety is surprising. My wife's suet bar
and feeding tray, swung on wires safe from squirrels, give
us right by the terrace door the company of nuthatches,
often upside down, tufted titmice, tom tits, we used to call
them, chickadees, nearly always upside down, black caps
on head, the delightful brown creeper forever spiralling
round a tree. What a long curved bill he has to do his
exploring with. Downy woodpeckers, too, are always there.
Or are they hairy? We're not experts enough to tell. They're
friends anyway.

Across the lane jays flash in the sun above the water
regardless of cold, their colour a match for the bluest sky.
Now and then we catch a fleeting picture of the red-
shouldered hawk as he glides without the whisper of a
sound through the fringe of trees by the brook. He looks
immensely large in winter, a ghostly sort of bird seeming
to float rather than fly. One day towards spring as I passed
below the mill dam, one of them rose suddenly and drifted
away, silent as ever, a three-foot struggling snake clutched
in his talons. It was like an Audubon painting come to life.
There is a chance, of course, that this may have been a
Cooper's hawk.

Owls are with us all the year, but the whoo-hoo-hoo-hoo
of the barred owl carries far to us over the snow. He seems
to like the deep wood west of us. Perhaps we hear the great

horned owl as well. Both are hard to see and sound somewhat alike, although the barred owl's hoot is far more varied. Little screech owls haunt the fringe of apple trees along the west lane. We hear them, too, more noticeably in winter.

Closer by, most intimate of our friends, are the cardinals. They're finches really. All winter long they live in a tangle of climbing rosebushes and bare forsythia on the slope back of the kitchen, no weather too rough to still their cheerful talk. I can hear my wife conferring with them every day in whistle language which bird and lady seem to understand.

English sparrows shelter everywhere, especially in the spruce trees. We rather wish that they would not as they are tough little Cockneys and want the whole place for themselves. Even at that, they add life to a winter day. Song sparrows everybody loves. They, too, prefer the shelter of the spruces by the barn where they and the juncos and the tree sparrows dine each day on seeds of wild asters, goldenrod, yarrow and the like where we have left a patch of slope to the wildflowers. Strangely many people, especially the poets, attribute song to the female in birds. It is the male, however, who really sings.

Horned larks are a treat for we love to see a winter flock of them rise suddenly from a meadow where the snow has melted. They look so alert and cheerful that it comes as a surprise to hear their plaintive whistling note so forlorn it is.

Snow buntings, the snowflakes, are rightly named, for with us they come and go with the storms from the north. Some years we see none of them. When we do, they give the impression of being blown about by the weather and liking it. Though sparrows, they are shy, unlike their more companionable cousins.

WE ALWAYS CONNECT the crow with hounds draw-
ing covert or at the end of a long day's run, for it is then
that crows delight to mob a new-found or a sinking fox.
I had a perfect example of this three days after Christmas
last year, as I watched the Pickering draw a finger of woodland near Croftridge. From where I stood by a fencerow,
I could see clearly across stubble to the edge of the copse
300 yards away. I could hear hounds speaking now and
then well up to my right and deep in the wood. A touch
or two of the huntsman's horn floated down to me, and
his voice as he cheered them to a find. With luck I'd view
the fox, for the wood ended just opposite me. It would be
hard to miss him if he broke from covert there and crossed
the open. That is just what he did do. Light as a shadow,
he slipped from the trees, glided a few rods straight on,
then cut back, slanting across the stubble between me and
the wood, heading more or less to his right. An old trick
and a clever one. I was not going to betray him—not for a
while at least. But the crows did. Two of them suddenly
burst from the treetops where they had been spying and
stooped like falcons with wild sarcastic cawings to the
fox. He put on speed, knowing well what such talebearing
spelled for his scheming. The two crows were flying low
now, not a yard above his back, shrieking like demented
banshees.

It would be a poor huntsman and a mighty deaf one to
boot, if he could not hear their clamour. Almost at once
I caught the sound of his voice and the crack of the whipper-
in's thong as he turned hounds to the horn. Instead of
working slowly through the wood on the line of the fox,
the pack was galloped straight to the sound of those knavish
crows, saving three-quarters of a mile of hunting and a
certain check where the fox had turned. Only when they
heard the cry of the pack owning the new line did the
crows cease from their mobbing, mission accomplished.

What a picture I carry of that winter's morning—fox-wit, crow-wit, man-wit. In the end the fox gave hounds a comfortable burst, then went to ground in a drain by Valley Hill where he could mock at them all.

Like crows, starlings love company and go about in flocks. I must say we detest them even in winter. In summer, however, they are death to Japanese beetles and that is something in their favour.

Cock pheasants, with us the year round, come into their glory when the leaves are down. Originally they were ringnecks, but a good deal of the English pheasant strain has been introduced. They must carry a lot of scent, for hounds occasionally will speak to their line. Young entry especially are inclined to riot of this sort. And so are the beagles. Once hounds give tongue, up go the birds like an exploding bomb.

THOUGH NOT ALWAYS with us and really a spring bird, the little blue heron shows up now and then to wade in the brook where the wild duck come and the great Canada geese. What the heron finds to feed on in the chilly days of spring we cannot imagine, for surely there are no frogs about then and not many fish. Herons have a stately look as they stand so pensively by the water or in it. We like them. Once in a while we see the blue heron in its young pure white plumage. It is easy then to mistake it for the snowy egret. Visitors often exclaim over the blue heron in his white coat telling us excitedly that they have just seen an egret. We doubt it.

THOUGH NORMALLY a summer boarder, the turkey buzzard, by rights a vulture, floats and soars through most of our winter skies. How the gliding and the slow, sure

turns used to fascinate me as a boy as I'd lie on my back
and watch them from the comforting shade of a blackberry
bush.

Empty? Our countryside? Sky and field and stream and
copse throb with life the year round. All one has to do is
look.

> *A poor life this, if full of care,*
> *We have not time to stand and stare.*

We stood and stared all right the day after Christmas,
my wife and I, as we watched the Eagle hounds find their
fox on Black Horse Hill. Later, in the lane near the kennels,
it was a vixen; she broke to view again from the wood below us on the right, swept up the slope, dropped into the
lane and trotted straight towards us, all her attention on
the hounds below. The fox never saw us until she was
twenty yards away. When she did, she stopped for an
instant, then sprang up the left-hand bank and disappeared,
going to earth safely enough twenty minutes on by Lower
St. Matthew's. A moment after she had crossed the lane,
hounds were spilling into it making the whole glen ring
with their music.

Things like this are but the smallest part of winter's
pageant. As far as foxhounds go, the best of it is that the
sport is not and never has been with us a pastime solely
for the wealthy with time and money to spare to it. Local
farmers are among the keenest riders we have. Nor has
age much to do with it either. Jamie, at fifteen, was going
cross-country with the best. The last of the year he and I
went over to follow the Cheshire a bit by car. While there,
I introduced him to the squire of Runnymede, with sixty
years of hunting to his credit, yet still sharing more of the
chase on his cob than most of the field. It was a joy to see
again the old-time sheen, the well-boned leather of his
boots.

BACK AT HOME more mundane chores were waiting. Young Clarence, our summer bean-picker, and I got to work clearing the wooded bank along the road. I'd been intending to police that confounded bank for a long while but kept putting it off. Now, leaves down, we had a good crack at it one day, piling up dead wood and fallen limbs and burning them. How easy it is to keep things right; how hard to get them so. Platitudinous but true, especially in our case where all the work had to be done by ourselves, save for the help we could get now and then from Horace and the boys nearby. Clarence worked hard, wearing the scarf my wife had given him for Christmas.

ALMOST EVERY WEEK now some work was done along the lane, burning branches that had collected there for years. It proved a chore that lasted through the winter. John came over from Wallingford week after week on Saturdays to help at it, a little at a time. As we worked, a cardinal—they like company—used to come over from the house to whistle and sing nearby. Friendly, it was, to hear him. A pair of bluejays must have had other things to think about as they screamed to one another above the creek, for they paid us no heed. Now and then we could hear the sweet cry of hounds on the hills or far off by Anselma meadows. Once or twice Jamie rode by, usually mud-splattered, home-bound after hunting with Orville. I must say it made John and me so envious at times that we'd just knock off our burning and go find hounds ourselves if we could.

John viewed his first fox this way, a dog fox breaking covert one midafternoon in January over by the Eagle. I think John was properly thrilled by it, for it is exciting the first time one hears hounds swell in chorus as they own the line of a new-found fox. And more exciting to view that

fox as he goes away! How old all this is. Three centuries
have gone since Shakespeare harked to the selfsame cry in
Warwickshire. It was he speaking, not Hippolyta, really:

"—never did I hear such gallant chiding—every region
near Seemed all one mutual cry. I never heard so musical
a discord, such sweet thunder."

S PITS OF SNOW, thaw and freeze; each winter's day
paints for us from a different palette. Now the far-off hills,
clear-cut, stand near at hand, the very tree trunks showing;
and now they sink into themselves, aloof, veiling the sky-
line, soft with mist, the slopes by Broadwater and Flowing
Springs as faraway and hidden as the Blue Ridge.

The colder it is, the more wintry the weather, somehow
we feel more keenly the itch to get on with our gardening.
It snowed the 11th of January and that was enough. We
ordered seeds for the coldframe, seeds for the borders and
seeds for the truck patch. That bewitched us. We even
ordered a martin house we knew we couldn't afford,
rationalizing the expense by filling it with martins—before
it came—and filling the martins in their turn with every
sort of beetle, pest and grub that could infest a garden.
They were suffering from bloat, those greedy martins of
our mind, even before their house was paid for, let alone
put up. Actually, when summer came, bluebirds not martins
took permanent possession of it, fighting off every other
bird that wanted a peep at it. Bluebirds are there yet. What
they may do to garden pests, we do not know, but we love
them anyway for the bit of sky on their wings as they turn
and lift in the sun.

Spurred to more activity by the snow and the glory of
the cardinals against it, I found a bale and a half of peat
moss hidden away in the barn where I should have left it
till spring. Did I? Ah, no. On it must go where the wild-

flowers were blanketed too deeply already. Midwinter madness is tickle o' the sere. Once it starts, it's hard to control. Usually a new catalogue, fantastic in colour, is all that is needed to touch us off. A really rugged day, thermometer at zero, has much the same effect.

WHILE ORDERING SEEDS and wondering what havoc we had done to the wildflowers, we suddenly thought of the martin-colony pole. We'd clear forgotten that. Fifteen feet of cedar didn't seem very high on paper, but when it arrived it looked like the mast of a ship, a ship-of-the-line at that. Naturally we waited till John could help get it up. We always had to wait for him when puzzled or helpless. And never once did he fail us.

One day in Iceland during the war a ship survived the gauntlet of the U-boats and reached Reykjavik with a mixed cargo aboard, all in the greatest demand. Among other things there was the mast for a fishing vessel, priceless past telling, for there is no wood of size in Iceland. The mast had been ordered in the States, cut to size and prepared there and now had come to port safely at unthinkable cost. It was larger than our martin-house pole, I must admit that, but it didn't seem so, made fast on the deck of the ship. It was long, however, and so heavy that the dockers could not get it ashore, so they asked the general for aid. A young up-and-coming lieutenant was told to take a detail and see what they wanted.

In an hour he was back, beaming.

"What? You've done it already?"

"Yes, sir. No trouble. Anything else for the detail?"

"What did they want?"

"Just a big hunk of wood, sir. They couldn't get it clear of the rigging. Kind of a pole, sir."

"It's ashore?"

"Yes, sir. I sawed it in two. They'd never thought of that."

I think of the look on that young officer's face as the general enlightened him, for enlighten him he did, every time I see our mastlike pole with the flash of the bluebirds about it. Thanks to John, we got it up in one piece.

When the time came to rear our pole, however, trouble really began. Attaching the houses of the colony to the end of the pole was easy, for the long cedar was lying conveniently propped on two boxes. Digging a deep hole for it was not difficult either. Complications set in when we struggled to lift the now topheavy, fifteen foot monster and sink its butt gently where it belonged without jarring our top-hamper free. In the end, of course, we got it up and firmly set. I knew that we could do it, because whatever John tackles, he finishes, still smiling.

One thing both of us forgot. The boxes should have been given a coat of paint before the pole went up. They had white sides and green roofs, but the paint seemed a lick-and-a-promise affair at best. It soon peeled badly and flaked. Some day those boxes will warp. This year I have the second layer of houses on hand, waiting to go up. They've been well painted and will have all winter to weather in before the birds come in spring. Martins this time? Or will they be bluebirds again? Also, how in the world can we get the second-story boxes, painted though they be, properly set on the top of that pole? Whatever happens, we do not want to take it down.

The hitch of it is, however, how to paint the houses already up. We have no ladder that will reach so high. John at the moment is at sea, school over. Next fall he'll be at college. We'll manage though. Maybe Bill from the Corner can solve that one for us. Right now there is no hurry. The bluebirds are still in residence. Morning-glory vines are clambering close to the top of the pole, turning our mast

into a thing of beauty, even if it won't be a joy forever.
One thing is sure. We'll not dig it up and try to replant it.
That would be the wormwood and the gall!

IN MID-JANUARY, realizing that Noel would be
through school this spring and not available with his tractor,
I went over to see some neighbours of ours about the possibility of their working the fields for us and getting in oats
with our usual cover crop of timothy, alfalfa and brome-
grass. Two brothers farm their place, and better handled
land it would be hard to find anywhere. They live in an
old stone house with their parents over Uwchlan way, a
house that their ancestor built in 1712 when he came to
these hills from overseas. The floors are worth going miles
to admire, for they are as sound as the day they were laid.
Great 12- and 14-inch planks they are, some oak, some
poplar. When the floors were laid, the boards, cut from
the natural taper of the trees, were laid alternately end to
end, so that the narrow end of one plank joins the wide
end of its neighbour and fits like tongue-and-groove along
its length, thus keeping the combined width of two boards
equal at both ends. Hand-hammered nails, with flattened
heads a half-inch wide, were used in the old house with
wooden pegs to pin the great beams where they are mortised
like the framing of a barn.

When they built in those days, they built, as Eugene
built his bridge, to stay. After 242 years, that house is as
sturdy and true as the hill stones that went to its walls. We
were lucky to make arrangements with these brothers for
in one spring's tilling they have changed the whole look
of the place and they have done so most fairly in cost.

As I drove back from their house, thinking of the history
its long span had covered, my mind turned to the cost of
the work at home and how best we could pay for it. That

led me to thinking of all the strange money man has used for exchange in our county since farming began. While the walls were going up in the old house I had just left, Indian wampum was a form of legal tender here. Though the Swedes and the Dutch no longer controlled the Delaware, styvers, guilders, pistoles, pieces of eight and moidores were current, as court records show. They sound a good deal more like Treasure Island than Uwchlan. A pistole equalled one pound, eight shillings. A moidore passed for two pounds and four shillings, a large sum in those days.

Up to the Revolution, pounds, shillings and pence were the currency most used. Spanish-milled dollars, familiar then and surely carrying an old-fashioned ring about them, are still in use when old deeds call specifically for payments in such specie. I'm told that the banks keep a small supply of them on hand for this purpose. When the ground rent, or whatever it may be that must be paid in them, has been paid, the recipient promptly returns them to the bank which is glad to redeem them in current notes, keeping the old coins for the next year. A friend of mine marked a Spanish-milled dollar once and had it come back to him like an old friend year after year.

LONG AFTER the house at Uwchlan was built, barter was legal tender in our county, corn, barley, wheat, oats, tobacco, pork and beef being so listed at the market price. Of course, when I planned to sell my grain to the mill and get seed and fertilizer in return, barter was still in effect. We haven't changed so very much after all, not in the fundamentals. My grain, which I was mentally selling to the mill as I drove home from the farming brothers, was a little like the insects eaten by the martins before the martin house was up or the martins in it or even summer at hand. The wheat and the oats, of course, had not yet been seeded.

The fields for them had not been ploughed. Still it helps a lot to daydream. Every so often dreams come true.

Just to show that even a mild winter can bite, the temperature dropped to 4 degrees below zero before the end of January, freezing the pipe in the springhouse where water is pumped to the house. No water ran in the taps until we'd thawed the intake pipe with a blowtorch and rewrapped it with burlap feed bags. During the emergency the old spring in our cellar flowed calmly on and gave us all the water we needed, dipped up in a pitcher.

NOT FAR AWAY FROM US, up the lane, a friend of ours kennels a pack of basset hounds, sure and steady line hunters, with voices as deep as the bay of a bloodhound. Speed is not their forte. True line work is. Many of our neighbours, especially the young ones, like to follow this stout little pack on foot on a Sunday afternoon when they hunt rabbits. No harm is done to man or beast, but all enjoy it. Afterwards the field is often asked back to tea by the kind people at whose house the bassets met before the hunt.

ONE DAY IN JANUARY when the cold had broken, the meet was at Pippin Hill just up our lane. And so was the tea that followed it. High tea! Tea with an egg to it, as the Scots say. Everybody was there, including the Vicar. A steer had been killed for the occasion, and such hot roast-beef sandwiches were piled before us as never were on land or sea. How anything could taste quite so good, I don't know. And such quantities of everything! Cheese, fresh bread, pickles, jam and preserves, cakes and dessert and good cold beer—everywhere one turned there was something else more tempting to eat and each more toothsome than the last—except that incredible beef. Nothing could equal that. Young and old fell to upon it, some hungry from their running to hounds in the sharp winter weather. Some apparently just as hungry because they had stood at the meet and watched hounds start. And some, just because, like my wife and I, they couldn't resist a feast so good. Or friends so warmhearted. How the good lady at Pippin Hill made all this ready we don't know. One thing is sure. We learned that day what can be meant by festive board. There was no cliché here, for that is just what it was. Everybody was happy and showed it. No one who shared in the feast will ever forget it.

A week later, the cold spell really broke and grey squirrels showed one of the first hints of spring, pairing off and chasing one another madly over the thawing ground, a sign betokening early mating. We could see their dreys high up in the treetops, looking for all the world like crows' nests. Hit the butt of the tree sharply with the head of an axe and the scolding above soon proves who are the tenants.

With the thaw came a marked increase in the notes of the birds—not song yet; after all, it was still January, but a far more lively chattering. We do not always realize in summer how lovely the notes of a bird can be. There are too many of them. But in the chill of winter the cardinal's friendly, inquisitive whistling by the door, the low, cheery notes of the tree sparrow or the bravura of the song sparrow, undaunted by cold, come to us as special gifts. Of course, such gifts come in summer, too. As I write, I can hear the notes of the phoebe floating swiftly across the meadow of the mill dam. What could be more lovely? In winter, however, sound carries far when the ground is hard and trees are bare. We can hear crows scolding a hawk or an owl a miles away or more, but it is the neighbourly chitchat in the spruces by the barn that we like the best. After all, if spring is on the way, why not be told about it?

"He that is of a merry heart hath a continual feast."

7

BEFORE THE SWALLOW DARES

AS JANUARY CAME TO AN END, many a day I
looked up the slope, half expecting to see Eugene at work
with his brush axe or shears clearing a hedgerow or resting
in the winter sun, his back against the old stone wall—
time out for a smoke. Like most countrymen, he knew the
wisdom of slow pace with a rest now and then. Horace
works in just the same fashion. What both of them can
accomplish by the end of the day puts the let's-finish-it-now
ones to shame. *Festina lente* is a good motto for the land.

ALENA STAYS in our mind as much as her husband,
thanks to the fish problem, I suppose, as much as anything
else, apart from her own charm. We reached high-water
mark there one day when my wife brought home some
scallops for supper. Alena eyed them suspiciously.

"Thees not from river? Aha! Aha! From sea, Missus! I theenk eet!"

"You might try them. Eugene might like them, too."

"I do not theenk eet. Eugene—he iss—he not like change."

"Well, let him try them anyway. They're really good."

"Tcht! Tcht! My husban' he iss spoiled. His mother she spoil heem too long, I theenk. For me, eet iss the teeths."

Later scallops on the stove, Alena sat down suddenly.

"Missus! Missus! I am seeck!"

My wife, fearing a stroke, ran to the kitchen.

"Eet iss the mel-de-mer! Sea-seeck I haf! Thees feesh, Missus, they haf' me seeck. I cannot stant eet!"

After that, we gave up trying. Who can contend with mind over matter? Or is it the other way round? The very thought of anything from the sea was enough to floor them both.

O N   T H E   2 2 N D   O F   J A N U A R Y last year, in looking over my hunting diary, I made a surprising discovery. Just forty-one years before to the day, I had ridden that fine old hunter Forestus from Willisden in the valley to a meet of the Pickering hounds at their kennels. All this was new country to me then and a long way off. I'd never hunted with the Pickering before and had to start at 8:30, jogging fast to reach the midmorning meet in time.

How I had the vaguest idea of where we were going, I do not know, but there it was, each covert we drew written down four decades ago to be read now with amazement and delight. I must have plagued some long-suffering member of the field unmercifully, running down the name of every copse and hill and crossroad we came to—the kennels, Phoenix Hill, Hallman's, Charlestown Village. Two Church Hill, Gill's Shop, Pine Creek, Chester Springs, Anselma meadows, the long pastures by Byers—on to the find on Black Horse Hill at noon. Between Gill's Shop and Anselma, we had ridden Pine Creek Lane and drawn the woodland here at Melbrook. The hunt had long since passed from mind. I hadn't the slightest thought that I had ever ridden to hounds over our farm here, let alone so many years ago, until I chanced to read that faded old record. Then it began to come back to me.

I saw again the Master taking a heavy fall that day over post-and-rails somewhere in the valley below the Two Church Hill, I think it must have been. As his horse tore loose and galloped off, the M.F.H. was up as soon as he and running hard after him, his scarlet coat split wide up the back from the skirts to collarband. As he ran the coat-tails and the coat flapped wide on either side, giving him the look of a giant flamingo taking off in flight. Torn coat or not made no difference to that hard-riding, most gallant of Masters. Old Orville was the huntsman then. Young Orville, they called him forty years ago. Between them, they kept indomitably at it that day to the find and the glorious run that followed.

HOW MANY MILES we had ridden, Forestus and I, before the hunt was over and we had plodded back to Willisden, there is no telling, but tired the pair of us were. I can see the old horse now ramming his muzzle deep into a pail —sound wood, it was—and slushing about the warm thick gruel, bran mash, with a handful of oats stirred into it and half a bottle of whiskey to wet it down. Horses fared well in those days. When they'd covered sixty miles with a run thrown in, we felt they had earned their keep and a bracer as well. This, however, was a special treat. As I look back on it, the stableboys probably got more of the whiskey than Forestus, deserving it not at all. Wisely, I got none.

I hope Forestus has found still greener pastures and still keener hounds for company. I never knew a horse who loved their cry so dearly or who stayed with them more cannily. Actually he taught me, as a boy, all I knew of hunting. He'd pick the panel he thought we should take, deciding the moment he landed in a field just where we—I should say he—had best get out of it. He'd check instantly the moment hounds did, never stirring, then on with them the moment they recovered their line. Never once did he override or press them. Nor was he ever left lagging behind. He was the pilot; I the passenger well carried. Too well, almost, at times. One terrifying day when the old horse felt it best to get on with hounds regardless of hazard, I having nothing to do with it, he leaped four feet seven inches of wire and landed, with a drop, in a road, then cantered calmly on in the wake of the pack. Too scared to fall off, I had stuck my thumbs under the breastplate strap of the martingale and commended my soul to God as I felt him rise to that appalling wire. What memories I owe to him! What gratitude I owe the kind people at Willisden who let me hunt him now and then as a treat, for he was not mine.

On the anniversary of that day with the Pickering, it snowed here and grew bitterly cold, the ground icy. I thought how a little more snow before the cold would have kept the Max Graf roses warmer on their bank. Somehow they survived anyway. Ticked onto it by rough weather, we got at catalogues again and ordered some raspberry canes for spring planting. And strawberry vines—Horace promised to get them for us in good time. By then our hobby had the bit in her teeth, and we knew there was no stopping her once she had bolted. So we ordered a white rose-of-Sharon, a wychhazel, a silver-bell tree and a *Viburnum carlesi*—the Korean spice. We tried to get a *Viburnum fragrans*, but so far have had no luck in running one down. We did, however, order a chimonanthus—the wintersweet.

All of these, except the wychhazel and the rose-of-Sharon, have most lovely fragrance in spring. We were planning for scent now close to the terrace, just as we have planned for it in summer with the mint and the herbs.

LISTING ALL THESE PLANS of ours, ordering things so blithely, even growing some of them reasonably well, make it appear that our work here is simple or that we possess some magical right judgment in such things. Nothing could be further from the truth. It's easy for anyone to sit by a midwinter fire and dream of green things growing. To pass the waymark of these dreams is quite another story. We've been finding that out right along. We made—and are making—the most stupid of mistakes, looked at from hindsight.

For instance, we planted our Kousa dogwood in full sun and wondered for two years why the leaves were always baked and curling. We're going to move that Kousa this fall. Inquiry beforehand as to a Kousa's tastes would have saved that work and helped the tree to a better start. We sowed our lettuce row one year next to the bush beans, forgetful of drifting insecticide. Surely that was thoughtless. We even sowed it all in one row and all at one time the first year, thus eating lettuce for a spell in such disturbing quantities that one more leaf of it and we'd have grown rabbit's ears.

Just this summer, to show how dumb we can be, Bill and I spent many weeks felling walnut and ash saplings where they had overgrown a meadow near the spring. Always we look for a farm pond there one day. As we cut the trees, over 150 large ones, we piled them in immense heaps to dry for burning, but not till the foolish piling was half done did we realize we'd burn the barn down for sure and probably the house, too, if we tried to fire the trees where they were. All these piles must be moved this fall. There are seven of them! A double labour as well as a needless one. Why didn't we think?

Even more stupid was my folly this summer in spotting two great patches of Canada thistles springing up in the fallow strip we had left between two fields of oats to prevent erosion. I knew perfectly well from the day I saw them that I must get rid of those thistles before we ploughed the strip for wheat in fall. I knew they must be sprayed and scythed and burned before they came to head, or the seeds of next year's scourge would be blown far and wide. A child would know this and act on it. Yet somehow day by day slipped by till thistledown was floating, before young Bill and I left off our tree felling to burn them. I'm sure we were too late.

Other mistakes we have made were not so much stupidly done as in ignorance. We moved a good sweetshrub under a walnut tree and put some azaleas there. Neither are doing very well. We learned, though late, about walnuts. We had the drive resurfaced when we came here, then almost at once saw how badly we needed a light near the bend, where good friends smack into our apple tree trying to back out at night. Horace had to rip up the new drive and dig a trench across it for the wiring. Obviously we ought to have thought of that light long before we remade the drive. So it goes, but we are learning. Patience does it and good hard work.

Stones in the garden soil were another sample of our ignorance. Perhaps old Eugene was right when he'd cry, "Ston's? Where iss thees ston's?"

My thought was to rake the ground clear of every last pebble, leaving it swept and garnished like a company parade ground before Saturday's inspection. Our garden, however, is on a slope. Now stones, small ones, though we did not know it at the time, serve a twofold purpose on

slopes. They prevent a great deal of wash-off and unquestionably they tend to conserve moisture. Maybe that is why
Nature puts so many of them there. We are finding that
vegetables do better on their slope with a few stones left to
keep them company.

Probably our most natural mistake, everybody makes it
at first, has been to grow too much of everything. Next year
that lesson should bear fruit—should we say less fruit—for
we are doing away with most of the upper part of the
vegetable garden. This will leave us a patch one-third
smaller, yet quite large enough for our needs. Trying to
freeze enough food for a platoon and finding space to store
it all can defeat the whole purpose of our living here.
Enough is enough.

GARRY, LIKE MY GOOD WIFE, is a great conserver
of food. He wastes nothing. Not only does he have the
usual caches of buried bones as emergency rations, but he
saves everything that soaks into the flaps of his curly ears.
After his dinner, there's a regular routine as he sits down,
cocks his head on one side and lets an ear fall into his
mouth. This flap thoroughly cleansed, he licks his chops and
swings his head over to chew the other ear free of supper.
It's one way of doing it.

NOW IN MIDWINTER, our errors comfortably forgotten for a while, seeds and new shrubs ordered, Garry
and I took another walk on the hills. He lives for walks like
this in winter, as he does for swims in summer. How I envy
him! This time, however, the wind was biting more noticeably than usual on an ear frost-nipped high on Armanns-
fell in Iceland. Garry's ears, perhaps fortified by part of his

dinner, suffered no inconvenience at all. Finger bowls? Frostbite? Who knows?

THE LAST WEEK IN JANUARY we put in a busy afternoon by hunting with the Treweryn beagles from a Bellevue meet at 2:30 and seeing them start a hare from her form in the first ten minutes. They carried her at a lively clip downcountry, over Talhern slopes, then on towards Sugartown on the hill. At 3:30 we pulled out and hurried back in time for a meet of the Skycastle bassets at 4:00. This was right at home, not a mile up our lane. Pace was easier here. We could enjoy things more and pant less, although with the beagles I am, alas, a hill-topper these days. It is my wife who invariably views the hare and runs well to hounds. Now and again she puts a hare up not a yard from her feet. It's inconceivable how close hares can lie in their setts or forms. Fifteen couples of beagles and a field of fourscore will spread out and walk a field, drawing, so they think, each foot and furrow of it. Then, trying over precisely the same ground, hounds may put up two or three hare where none were seen before. Or my sport-loving wife may step on one—almost.

We had a good day with the bassets. Light was gaining now and we could stay at it longer. High tea and a snug fire at the Master's served to end our sport on the right note. Lest someone feel we had brutally torn harmless hare or rabbits to bits, it may be reassuring to know that no fur flew. Pursued and pursuers went happily home to their suppers.

ALBERT VAIL at the post office suffers from the same complaint as we do—love of seeing things grow. January had not passed before he, too, had given way to the seed

catalogue spell and was ordering more roses, although he
has masses of most lovely ones in his garden already.
Cardinals outside were whistling like mad now. Maybe that
had something to do with it. I knew just how he felt as he
told me about the new plants. I could see through the grille
the gardener's glint in his eye. That is unmistakable. This
was not a storm-and-cold phase of the urge we shared, but
what is even more fatal—the springlike, song-sparrow variety of magic that betrays us three months ahead of time.
Thunder and lightning, surely that means spring in the
offing, set us to rechecking catalogues almost before the real
nip of winter had touched us.

How lovely Christmas ferns can be in midwinter,
far greener, seemingly, than in summer when they are hidden by other growth. We have masses of them growing wild
on the steep bank across from the mill. As John and I
worked there, pulling dead wood clear and burning fallen
branches, we were careful not to tear up these ferns. We
knew how right a background they would make for the
thousands of spring-beauty, bloodroot and anemones that
cover this bank in the spring.

One of the miracles of the countryside is the way no
season can be jacketed into its own special calendar
months. The ferns, though green, spoke to us on a sharp
winter's day, but they also spoke to us just as surely of
spring ahead. The dead bracken fronds we were burning in
February were a part of last summer's pageant just as the
shrivelled goldenrod and ironweed stems were reminders of
fall. All the seasons interlock. All carry somewhere about
them a pledge of what is to come.

We can say in winter:

O, all ye green things upon the Earth, bless ye the
Lord: Praise Him and magnify Him forever,

just as we can sing in high summer of ice and snow, frost and cold, knowing in our hearts exactly what is meant. The canticle Benedicite Omnia Opera must have been composed by a good husbandman, so surely it speaks of the land and of the seasons in their cycle, praising, as they do, the Lord and magnifying Him forever.

THROUGH ALL OUR WORK on the bank, kingfishers kept sweeping over the water by the two-arched bridge that leads to the mill. A lovely bridge it is, of lichened stone. The kingfishers as usual ignored us. The cardinal never came down the lane to whistle at us near the mill. When, however, we worked the upper lane, there he would come each time. Starlings, whole murmurations of them, adorned the telephone wires beyond Arley cottage, not glamourous, but hinting of spring in their own harsh way. How these little things do count. Was it not Lord Tweedsmuir or his son who said, "Those who do not value small things are unlikely ever to be happy." How could they be?

WE SAW GOOD OLD ORVILLE one afternoon early in the month, as he stopped at the turn of the lane to sort out hounds. He and the Kimberton had held a joint meet that morning, running a brace of grey foxes hither and yon in the woodlands. Greys are maddening, always circling but never breaking covert if they can help it. Often they will climb a sloping tree like a squirrel. Really I suppose they are wise as can be.

How different are our points of view. We call the grey a cowardly, cringing scoundrel, unworthy of notice—because he has the wit to stay in covert and save his brush. The red fox, however—ah, he is a stout-hearted, gallant fellow! We're proud to hunt him to the death if we can—because

he is fool enough to leave the wood and risk hide in the
open. "Can honour set to a leg?" asks Falstaff.

THE KIMBERTON HUNTSMAN was using the old
curved cow horn slung over his shoulder by a thong. Orville had the straight English horn stuck in the front of his
hunting coat. What a time the pair of them had of it, getting the two packs sorted, Orville's to go home in his improvised hound van, the Kimberton finally jogging off at
their huntsman's heels, as he sounded deep notes on his
ancient horn. There is something primitive about the soughing of such a horn. It carries us back and across the seas.
I wonder for how many centuries it must have echoed for
our ancestors in the forest glades before the copper horn
was dreamed of. The sound of the cow horn gave us a
different picture to remember at Melbrook, as hounds and
huntsman trotted from view up the Nantmeal lane.

Next day light snow limned another memorable picture
near the bridge at Avon Lea. As I drove homeward in late
afternoon, snow had stopped falling and the light in the
west was a glory. Suddenly a cock pheasant in his pride
crossed the road ahead, pacing slowly to my right. On the
tip end of his tail feathers he carried a white patch of fresh
snow at least an inch deep, for all the world like the tag
of a dog fox's brush. How the snow got there would be
hard to tell unless the cock had been sheltering in a furrow, as they do, while it was snowing. In any event, the
snow patch stuck till the bird flew up to clear the offside
hedge. How odd we should remember things like that. Or
be made so lighthearted by them. Yet how fortunate!

SNOW HAD GONE by the time I reached Melbrook
and saw that the suet bar was empty. Nuthatches and tom-

tits are greedier now than ever. This is always true as we pass midwinter and seeds and grubs grow harder for them to find. Indeed, the hungry time for most birds seems to be on the eve of plenty, very early spring, when the worst of the year is over. Suet bar and feeding tray last no time at all these February days. That hint of spring made us think how soon work must start in the truck patch, so four tons of manure were piled up handy for spreading. One thing is sure. We weren't stinting the land much.

Next day John came over to help me broadcast some inoculated Buffalo alfalfa seed on the upper west field already seeded to wheat as cover crop. We have said that the wheat had been put in too late in November for alfalfa to go with it. Following the advice of the Conservation Agent, we tried our alfalfa now on the frozen ground in mid-February, hoping that the thaw and freeze of early spring might induce at least some of it to sink in the ground and root. Just what the result will be we don't know yet, but we're not too hopeful. The timothy and the brome-grass fortunately were seeded with the wheat and appear through the stubble to be doing fairly well. In any case, it seemed meet enough at the time to follow the expert's suggestions.

Later in the day, as John and I were clearing the lane— a chore perpetual it seemed—one of the brothers from Uwchlan drove by and we made final arrangements for the spring ploughing and seeding the oats. What a reputation those brothers have for sound farming and a care of the land. Months later, in early summer, I spoke to the people at the mill about their buying our grain and straw. When they heard who it was that had done the planting, they asked no more.

"O.K. by us. If those two brothers put your seed in, there'll be a crop and a right one. We'll take all you've got of it."

Later on this summer, the man we had had a year ago

came over again to bulldoze out a mass of poison ivy, honeysuckle and saplings that had spread ten yards and more the whole length of a hedgerow, eating away a potentially good field. The moment he saw our oats stubble with alfalfa showing through it, he asked who had changed the slope so quickly. Naturally he knew that I could not have done it alone.

"I might have guessed it. There's no one in the county better liked than those brothers and their father before them. Or finer at farming. They know land. Can't say that of everyone these days. You're lucky."

We know that we are. Our good fortune began that winter day when I had talked to them at Uwchlan and the afternoon when we had made our final arrangements as John was burning brush in the lane. How enviable it is to have earned the respect of the countryside as these brothers have. Everyone has a good word for them, far and near, whenever their names are mentioned.

WHAT WEATHER February can bring. It was 12 degrees the day John and I broadcast alfalfa. Two days later the thermometer touched 72 degrees. Such spells are lovely, but play havoc. Everything starts to grow. The trees of the Lord may be full of sap, but we don't want them budding just yet awhile. One thing we do love to see in flower this early is the Chinese honeysuckle cut outdoors and brought inside to open. A few sprays of it can fill a house with a breath of spring, coming with us, well ahead of forsythia and pussywillows. The miracle is that it can blossom at all, such dead, dry sticks its branches look when first brought in.

Another fetcher in of green is the retinospora that fill the vases on the library chimney piece. We put the branches there at Christmas in water. By Easter they are just as fresh.

Then, too, all winter long the window trays keep something of summer with us. They hold the old faithfuls—geraniums, begonias, impatiens and sweet-scented paper narcissus, white grandiflora and golden soleil d'or mostly. Plenty of sun and my wife's green fingers made the library bay like a watered garden—until one warmish day when someone aired the room and forgot to close the window. That did it!

Nipped leaves, drooping stems—not all the loving-kindness nor all the repentance in the world could save some of them. Scissors, however, severe surgery and a gaining light brought wonders of healing to those not killed outright. It wasn't long before the windows were gay again.

THE 18TH OF FEBRUARY we heard the killdeer crying and knew that spring would not be long. They are plovers, these long-legged, graceful birds. We love to see them wheeling low over a meadow, usually near water. No bird we know can try as hard to lead trespassers from the nest which is always built on the ground. Day after day in early spring we used to pass a stretch of road near Firethorn where the nearside ditch had flooded till it formed a little pool. The killdeer nest must have been near it, for always the birds were there, fluttering ahead of us, dragging a wing, to steer us clear. Just to catch the first poignant killdee, killdee-dee-dee! in spring is tonic to the soul. Who can forbear a look at the toolshed then?

ABOUT THE MIDDLE OF FEBRUARY we planted the silver-bell we had ordered earlier. This is a lovely tree, as sweet in blossom as any. We hope it does well set near the front terrace in partial shade, yet getting the morning sun. At the same time we put a Chinese wychhazel, *Hamamelis mollis,* on the bank near the vegetable garden, with a native wychhazel near it. So far, the latter has done well, facing up bravely to this year's drought. The Chinese variety has had a rough time of it, mostly because we neglected to water it regularly. That oversight remedied, it seems to have picked up considerably and now is in good leaf. How crucial the first summer is for all transplanted trees and shrubs.

One thing may have set it back at the start. We were hurried the day we put it in, racing the dark. Naturally we made a poor job of it. Then, next day, our conscience got to work and nagged at peace of mind until the poor bush was dug up and planted properly. The moving could not have helped it much.

In our work here we have found that two things do more harm than all the rest lumped together. The first is rushing the game, striving to cram two days' work into one, for this invariably results in waste of both days. The second trouble-maker is to let other jobs distract us from the first, when there is no reason for it. Again and again, I vow never to yield to that folly, only to find myself throwing down the hoe or whatever it may be to yank some miserable weed from the okra three rows on. I see it there out of the corner of my eye, even when I try not to notice it. The more I ignore it, the more brazenly it flaunts its presence. I feel my-self yielding as I say to myself and to the horrible weed, "Mind your business! I'll tend to you soon enough!"

I know that I'll get to that row and that weed in good time. They can wait. But no, the thing draws me like a lodestone rock. I despise myself, but go over and snatch up the distractor, probably breaking it off at ground level in my anger, thus assuring a sturdier growth next time. On my way back to the hoe, I see a wild carrot by the garden's edge or in another row and must get after it as though life depended on it. It may be half an hour before I am back at my hoeing where I should have stayed all along. It's this rushing about that frays the nerves. We're learning our lesson, however, taking Horace and Eugene as perceptors. Sufficient unto the day makes good sense.

ONE TASK really called for a lot of time and left us well scratched and scarred. We have a great cluster of roses here, old, long-planted climbers, that cover a rock. The last ice age probably left us this boulder. Beautifully weathered it is and wonderfully shaped by wind and water. The roses, however, hid it completely, reinforced by a tangle of wisteria. We knew the time had come to wade in and prune. Prune savagely. I doubt if those roses had been cut back for years. Thorns bit like scorpions, but we kept at it until we had uncovered the rock.

All the wisteria was grubbed up—or that was our fond intent. With wisteria one never gets quite everything out. Only this morning I had to drag up three shoots of it, determined as ever, forcing their green way through the roots of the roses.

Once the rock was really clear of its blanket, we were glad we had pruned so deeply, for now one could see the great size of it and how lovely its colour really was. When spring came and the roses budded, the fresh green of their leaves found perfect foil in the grey of the boulder. It was not hidden now nor was it bare. Still later, when the blossoms had added colour, we knew the pruning had been cheap at the price, but in February, ripped and torn by the thorns, we were not so sure.

WHILE STRUGGLING with the rose tangle, we spied the first of our snow crocuses in flower, just peeping through the leaves at the edge of the rock, where, I imagine, some warmth is reflected to lure them on. The sight of them sets the leaven of spring to working in our bones if anything does. Robins, the first we had seen nearby, were nest hunting in the sycamores. It really was like Easter, although the calendar showed mid-February.

That afternoon my wife and I piled load after load of rose canes on an old bed-tick and dragged them to the burning. It is surprising what a cumbrous lot can be carried handily on a tick ripped open and spread to its full size. That old tick seems to fill a great many functions here at Melbrook. We use it constantly to drag leaves to the compost piles in fall. We used it now to lug away the thorny rose prunings. Its primary assignment seems to be to drape my old tandem cart stored away in the barn.

BY WASHINGTON'S BIRTHDAY birdsong was everywhere. The fields of young barley had taken on their yellow-green, gosling look of spring. Willow-whips were everywhere, brought down by the wind. What a sloppy tree the willow is before the surviving whips turn to fairy swaying wands. In the woodlands most of the oak leaves had gone, only the beeches retaining some of their tenacious yellow foliage, brittle, vibrating in the slightest breeze, but holding fast, as they would hold, until the new leaves pushed them off.

Taking advantage of frost-free ground, I dug a hole and fertilized it, to be ready for the Korean spice when it came. That done, my wife and I celebrated by going to a meet of the Pickering in the meadow below Springhead. In honour of Washington's Birthday, the field had turned out bravely, an unusual number of scarlet coats brightening the holiday fixture. Foxes, however, seemed unappreciative, for they proved hard to find. Hounds made up for that in part by crossing the brook in front of our house, sixteen or seventeen couples of them plunging into the water together to swim the stream. How those vignettes of the countryside are

imprinted on our minds, trivial things, yet remembered,
bright-cut with life and beauty. The colour of that passing
moment would be hard to describe. Hounds splashing into
the stream against a background of cedars on the slope
above, the grey walls of the old mill below, a cluster of
scarlet at the bend in the lane where the field were waiting,
wove for us a tapestry time cannot stale.

As the hunters rode off, I thought of Washington and his
devotion to the chase. On the wall of our library there hangs
the head of a white-tailed Virginia deer hunted by him from
Gunston Hall, not far downriver from Mount Vernon.
Naturally there are few things we value more.

How LITTLE we can picture simplicity of life then,
the impossible handicaps the leaders of the Revolution had
to face. A good example of this is the county-wide assess-
ment of silver made for taxing purposes in 1777, well before
the real pinch of the war had begun. In our particular township of Pikeland the assessors reported twelve silver tea-
spoons, six silver tablespoons and one silver coffeepot. That
was all. Surely the good people on the land didn't cater to
luxuries. Pewter, I suppose, and earthenware, an iron pot or
two and stout wooden trenches served them well enough.
Yet it was from such simple folk and from such sparsely
furnished dwelling places that the riflemen came who stood
their ground against the Grenadiers. They carried a brand
of fortitude in their hearts worth more to them—and to us—
than silver spoons.

How frugal, yet how complex in its way, life must have
been in these hills. For instance, to live at all, the men and
women on the land had to sell or barter what they raised in
excess of their own family needs. This meant some means
of transportation. In the very early days, before the turn-
pikes came, and the King's highways like the Great Lancas-

ter road and the Conestoga, grain was carried to the mill in sacks slung crosswise over a horse's back. Women, in whose province were the milking sheds and the poultry runs, used to ride sidesaddle to the nearest market carrying butter pails and panniers full of eggs and chickens, their horses bearing load and lady just as the grain was borne to the gristmill. Later, well before the Revolution, peddlers appeared. Petty chapmen, they were called in those days. These, too, rode long before they drove. Apart from what they had to sell, their main purpose was to collect the surplus at each farm, small things they could carry in panniers or in carts when they had them. In short, the chapmen or hawkers were middlemen. The word chapman is interesting, for it is derived from the same Anglo-Saxon source as our word cheap. Originally it mean to buy or sell and had nothing to do with the price of a purchase.

I thought of such things on Washington's Birthday and marvelled again at what he and his men had accomplished. A few miles away at Valley Forge, the great memorial arch there is inscribed with a phrase he once used in tribute to his forces, reduced at the time to a pitiful handful. I know of no more moving words anywhere.

"Naked and starving as they are, we cannot enough admire the incomparable patience and fidelity of the soldiery."

It puts us in good heart to know that some of those of whom he spoke were men from the hay meadows of the Pickering and the slopes of the Uwchlan hills.

WILD DUCK were on the pond above Pebble Spring by the end of February. They may have been there right along. Red-winged blackbirds had joined our robins now. The spot of colour of their shoulders reminds us of collegiate hood and gown, only the birds have the advantage of being more sprightly than academic processions. We've never seen a red-wing plod.

Closer by, periwinkle along the drive had shown encouraging glimpses of blue; bits of sky to hearten us. Mouse-eared chickweed had been blossoming for some time near the terrace, a regular suntrap these days. This is a weed all right, but also it's a flower and one of the first, so we let it grow for a while. Most of the spring we fight it tooth and nail. Yellow sorrel soon joined it by the library door.

LAST YEAR'S garden was far from a memory, for the deep-freeze still gave us quantities of peas, bush beans, okra, lima beans, squash and corn on the cob, as tasty, it seemed, as the hour they were plucked. Maybe we are prejudiced. The larder bulged with tomatoes and tomato juice we had had put up. Beets, carrots and onions held out to March.

At February's end, we began work on the garden. My wife, now a masterhand at the rotary-plough, raked mulch from a third of the vegetable patch and worked the soil over with the plough. The mulch was then put back—a wise move it turned out later, for this year's really terrifying drought set in early and lasted long. The mulch over the freshly ploughed surface of the ground kept everything moist and workable until we were ready to plant it. We'd fondly hoped that the mulch might prevent erosion in heavy spring rains, only there weren't any spring rains, to speak of, after March.

FRESH ENDIVE was ready in the coldframe now. We'd nursed it along all winter. The last day of the month the snowdrops, February Fair Maids, opened under the walnut tree near the terrace. We'd not been expecting them for quite a while yet. It is odd how flowers come in spring. The snowdrops in the shelter of the great rock, where the first crocuses are, should have come first but they did not. Those by the walnut, though far more exposed to wind and weather, blossomed well ahead of them. It's hard to tell. That's half the fun of it.

As planting time drew near, Garry and I shared many an hour on the slope above the house, seeing what the wheat was up to. I must admit that it looked sparse and spindly. No sign of the alfalfa had appeared, of course, nor of the timothy and brome-grass. No time of year can appear quite so bleak and hopeless as the last fortnight of February and the first two weeks of March. That is really the dead interval, although on the surface only. In reality life is stirring as at no other time, if we'd only look. There's plenty to see. Plenty to do. Garden and field work lie just ahead.

Each move here seems to be dictated by the old ways. Horace is an expert on such complexities. Light of the moon? Dark of the moon? They call the tune for spring seeding. Horace knows weeks ahead just when the moon will be in its right phases for peas and lettuce and spinach, beans and limas, things growing upward towards light; and for beets and carrots, radishes and onions, all that root downward towards dark. Under his guidance, we are learning a lot. Another old friend keeps us informed of weather ahead by what is happening now. For instance, we were told the other day that mist in August means snow at New Year's. We'll have to check on that one.

WHAT A HEAVY RAIN the first of March may foretell, we do not know, but this year it proved the last real soaker till August. On that March day, however, we were off to a good start. Torrential rains fell with high winds lashing the downpour to fury. Garry loved it, chasing mad, whirling leaves over the lawn to his heart's content. Most leaves are winter-soaked or brittle by spring, but those from the buttonwoods are tough as tanned leather. The storm set them to dancing from under every bush where they'd bided their turn. Garry, *ventre à terre*, made the most of it—as vain a pursuit as chasing his birds, but apparently just as much fun.

Across the lane the stream sang high in spate, one little waterfall near the bridge roaring over its dam-breast and pretending it was a river, while the millpond below, much of it usually silted and dry, widened once more to a sizeable lake. A wild March day, coming in like a lion but glorious to be out in. After all, a soaking is soon cured.

As the storm blew itself out the countryside had changed. Alder and aspen catkins were bursting by the brook. The tips of maple twigs in the marsh near Arley were ruddy as port. Grass had suddenly come green overnight. Next day there were ice on the puddles and a knife in the wind, but the lowlands were stirring. We'd made the turn!

"Thou visitest the earth, and waterest it:
Thou makest it soft with showers."

8

WINDS OF MARCH

WE WERE LUCKY in that rain; more so than we knew, for, as we have said, a dry spring followed, capped by the driest June and July on record. Now in March, after a winter of little snow, the heavy rain, three days we had of it, was doing the fields a world of good. We hear people say that rain runs off in dry weather and does not sink in. Mighty little of its runs off grass unless the ground is frozen. Regardless of the downpour, rain sinks in, slowed till caught by the millions of tiny blades. Better still, once in the ground it is held there by the roots of the sod. Trees on slopes perform the same function, only their root systems store even more water.

We are fortunate here for every year more farmers pay heed to conserving their topsoil, following the example of the Conservation Area adjoining us. Mention has been made of strip-farming and contouring. Such things are seen every-where. The more there are of them, the less we see of muddy streams carrying plough lands away in every freshet.

THE HIGH WINDS that brought in March also brought down branches from the sycamores, dead ones mostly, but a few in sap. Both are troublesome to pick up and burn or save for kindling, but like most of nature's ways they have served their purpose, for this is her yearly pruning, her vert rights of loppage and toppage that keep her forests trim. Winter ice and March winds are the shears and prun-ing hooks she uses.

Cold was not through with us yet by any means. Five days after the storm, the millpond froze. Much ice formed on the slower reaches of the creek. Pools beside the barn-yard wall were solid with ice, tips of the daffodil spears showing through it. Yet in spite of this the green had come. Or is it the gold of earliest spring we notice first? Willow wands at any rate were golden now, swaying in the chilly air. Their green would come later as the winds lost some of their bite. Over near Pebble Spring, sheltered in the glen, jasmine was in flower. How welcome a sight that is. Rain had brought blossoms out on the bare stems. Rain and wind had also burnished the sky for us, turning it to silver by late afternoon. Blue would come tomorrow.

GARRY AND I always seem to find something to do on the hill. Maybe it is because we like so much to climb it. This particular day we unearthed a rail from the fence up there, hidden in the hedgerow. It had been pulled loose way back at Hallowe'en when I'd replaced it with a spare. Now, however, the missing rail showed up, so I lugged it down to the barn for safekeeping. Sound rails are costly these days. We've none to throw away. Garry's ideas of being helpful are debatable, but help he must, even if his share of the job was to grab the hind end of the rail and tug it furiously in the wrong direction. Sometimes his weight and four feet dug in, plus determination and *joie de vivre,* won out and we swayed back a step. Sometimes the down slope favoured me and we swayed forward a step, weaving back and forth till somehow we reached the barn, the fence rail standing up to the strain better than I did.

BY THE END OF THE FIRST WEEK in March, bluebirds were flashing above the little orchard. Our dwarf trees must have proved a disappointment, for what the bluebirds seek in spring is an old tree with holes ready-made for their nesting. The martin house on its pole, however, soon caught their fancy, for they've been there ever since. We like to hear their little song, a quavering note but a happy one.

How everybody puts on new clothes in spring. It wasn't Easter yet, but we glimpsed a fox one day and never in all my life have I seen a coat so red or with as high a sheen to it as his. All the young springs since creation's dawning showed in its sleekness, as he trotted along, cocksure of himself in every inch. I'm certain he had a lady friend nearby and was sporting the best of his wardrobe to please her.

A little later the opening notes of the hounds made him put on pace, but in no wise did it disturb him. That coat was not going to be muddied for his tryst, hounds or no. It wasn't for he lost them in no time.

WHAT HORROR a new turnpike can cause. It's one thing when such roads kill the fools who race their curves.

We're better off without them—the fools, I mean, for they sometimes kill others as well as themselves. It's quite another story when hounds are run down or deer slain needlessly, as they are in surprising numbers. I suppose the authorities divide up the venison between them. Who is to say them nay? The day we viewed the sleek-coated fox, he must have crossed our own particular horror northwest of Bacton Hill, for the pack raced for it on a burning scent. Two people in a car saw the point the fox was making and somehow, thanks to a farm lane, managed to reach the wire fence beside the turnpike in time. Three or four couples of hounds had leaped the fence already and were casting about on the concrete roadway where scent had failed them, foiled by the oil and the fumes of cars which sweep along this road at seventy miles an hour. One man, at the obvious risk of his life, climbed the fence and ran to the middle of the road to wave down oncoming motors, while the other grabbed hound after hound and slung them by main force to safety over the wire. Soon the huntsman galloped up and rallied the pack to his horn. It was touch and go, but not one hound was lost.

I must admit the cars in this case slowed down, once they had sensed the emergency we could not prevent. One truck driver, bless him, jumped out to help. The fault of all this lies in the fencing. When the turnpike established its right of way, assurances were given that the road would be fenced properly against game as well as livestock. This has never been done. It probably never will be.

As HUNTING neared the end of the season, early gardening increased in tempo. My wife had already seeded her cabbage and cauliflower in flats. The garden itself was ready and waiting—on the moon. Horace kept us in check there. He isn't the man to stand any nonsense. Old ways have proved their metal. He would—that is to say, we would—stick to them with no newfangled flipperies.

As we waited, eager for first peas to go in, the cold held and the moon would not be hurried, but winter aconite, the wolfsbane, flowered under the walnut tree and violets bloomed in the shelter of the terrace wall. Almost mid-summer, it seemed. Surely high time for our peas. For radishes, at least. Horace was adamant, steering us clear of such heady pitfalls.

"St. Patrick's Day's the time. Got to wait. Got to be patient. Look at the moon yet! They'd just rot now."

We waited, though not so philosophically as Horace. His word is law here. It well should be. When we follow it, green things leap from the ground. Waiting was hard though, especially when the peepers woke and began shrill chorusing from the meadows near Anselma. We always hear them there before anywhere else.

THIS SPRING we noticed for the first time in years that red squirrels were increasing. Greys are always with us, summer and winter. We see a good deal of the little chipmunks with their dark-striped jackets. But red squirrels, once so numerous, had almost disappeared. Now apparently they are coming back. We're glad to see them. Greys are not too destructive here, but in England, where they have been introduced recently, they've proved an alarming menace. Whole orchards are stripped bare of their fruit or nuts by their pillaging. Indeed, so rapidly have they spread and so far-reaching is the damage they are doing that a bounty is paid for their destruction. It is the old story over again. When animals or plants which are useful or at least innocuous in their homelands are transported to another, almost invariably trouble results. Often such in-troductions occur by accident or carelessness, but the grey

squirrels seem to have been brought to England intention-
ally. Just why, nobody is sure. The country is paying a
price for it. Ecology brooks no tampering.

THOUGH NOT YET St. Patrick's Day, we prepared
for it by putting up one row of wire netting for our first
double row of peas. The wire was 100 feet long and 4 feet
high. It proved a tedious job to stake and fasten. Thanks
again to Horace, who would countenance wire but not peas
just yet, we got the fence up in time. Another year we'll
go back to sticks for peas. They make a wider support
and hold the vines up better. Also, spreading them more,
they facilitate picking. We can save our spring-pruned
branches and use them as we did the first year.

About this time we had a look at the old asparagus bed.
Nothing showed above ground, but things were stirring
below the surface, just to tip us off. Winter cover was
raked to one side, the bed was limed and fed, then cultivated about three inches deep. Even at that, we snapped
off a few of the more adventurous spears thrusting towards
the light.

How our neighbours do chuckle over that old bed. They
say we lavish far more care on it than we do on Garry
and spoil it just as much. I must admit there has been a
deal of pampering, but then there has been a good deal
of asparagus, too.

STILL ITCHING to risk the moon and St. Patrick,
we were tempted to get in a few peas regardless, but
Horace's influence went too deep. We refrained. We did,
though, get a start with flowers, emptying the terrace jars
of their old earth and refilling them. Snow crocuses had
opened now by the library wall, weeks after their earlier

relations near the rock. None of our daffodils had come to blossom yet, but some along the road by Diamond Rock were well ahead of ours. How one gets to know, year by year, the favoured nooks where first things show. Such places stick in the mind and draw us back—just to see what this year will bring.

It was still cold enough for an open fire of an evening, so more wood was brought over from the barn. The pile the Dobson brothers had stored for us on the terrace had lasted all winter. How handy it was to have wood there, dry under its tarp, yet only a yard from the library door.

ONE THING we could do in the frosty weather—that was put in half a dozen angle-iron fence stakes to hold the wires for our raspberries when they were planted. It's a blessing that a bit of winter holds over for a while. Otherwise, we'd be swamped by the onrush of spring. The raspberry site attended to, we found time to take the wire netting from our fruit saplings. Not a hare had come near them. Not a foot of snow had banked them, let alone the metre which Eugene had so surely predicted.

"One metre! Always one metre—snae! In Ukraine—"

The trees, however, had been chewed and knocked about a bit on top by deer. Next winter we must get some deer-deterrent spray. The Department of Agriculture recommends one.

MARCH 17TH CAME AT LAST. So did Horace—at earliest dawn—to help us with the peas. This year, he assured us, was certain to be lucky, for moon and St. Patrick both were co-operating. We couldn't possibly plant peas at a time more auspicious. Full moon would fall on the 19th, just two days on. Could we ask for more? While

at it, we put in early spinach, lettuce and radish, a third
of a row each. We also got in our onions, yellow and white.
To make a busy day complete, we planted our Cumberland,
Newburgh and Latham raspberries which had arrived in
time. This work, unfortunately, was rushed, edged in at
the busy day's end. We should have known by now how
little that would pay. Raspberries like a good start, with
a well-spaded trench and plenty of rotted manure worked
deeply into it. Time was short. We should have waited for
tomorrow, but we didn't. In went the root stocks higgledy-
piggledy. As a result, quite a few of them died. We learned
another lesson from that. How wise we'll be one day. Or
will we?

Soon afterwards, the last of our Colonial roses arrived.
It was no trouble at all to get them in, planted beside those
we had put in last fall. We were busy as beavers now, as
the weather relented and heartsease sprang up to speed us.
Sweet peas were sown by the library wall, the heat-resistant
variety, mixed. Wild life was everywhere, easily seen, as is
always the case in spring before the leaves have come to
hide it. Wild duck and the great Canada geese seemed
especially plentiful. We love to see them on the water
across the way or coasting in for a landing on the brook by
Far Fields. It is more thrilling to watch a wedge of geese
honking north than it is to see them southbound in fall.
After all, spring is a symbol of life returning. We rally to
that.

ON THE 22ND OF MARCH, three days before Lady
Day, daffodils opened at Melbrook, with the *Chionodoxa*,
glory-of-the-snow, coming two days later. Gold and blue,
what glorious colours they are! Forsythia had been partly
in flower before this. Now it answered the sun to give us
its best.

We put on pace ourselves. We had to. Trees were pruned and sprayed. A great dead willow was cut down near the springhouse—only its stump was not nearly so dead as we supposed it was. By late summer, the butt was a mass of new shoots sprouting, a trick willows have. To cut and split the huge three-pronged trunk of that willow and burn what we could of it, saving the best for firewood, cost John a lot of sweat.

PIPPIN HILL should be called Friendship Farm these days. March had not passed before we were given quantities of Persian lilac shoots from there for transplanting here. Not only did they thrive, but they have blossomed for us their first year in.

In spite of light snow on the 31st, grape-hyacinth and the windflower were in blossom, showing no ill effect from the cold. Along the terrace ha-ha, we had plenty of colour—pansies and violas vying with the Johnny-jump-ups. Those pansies have been miraculous this year. In spite of the drought, they bloomed well into November. Usually, the violas last longer but not this year. Naturally, we watered the pansies and all the terrace borders regularly and kept at it as we never have had to do before. *Phlox divaricata*, the wild sweet William, had not opened yet, nor had the mountain pinks or the candytuft, but all three were on the verge of it. That is the exciting time—just before things do open, when anticipation is at the highest.

WHAT VARIETY turns up on an old place like this. We were so captivated by the bricks on the terrace, especially by their mellowed colour, that we began hunting for more of them to brick the front terrace. That soon set off a chain-reaction that hasn't ended yet. The main block of the house here is high, too high to suit us. The library wing is too low. We were prevented from making it higher by a second-story window in the west wall that could not be sacrificed. Our problem has been to lower the house and raise the wing—at least to produce that illusion. We needed most of all horizontal lines across the front of the house. That was obvious. We needed them at little cost. That was even more obvious, as clear as a pikestaff by now without scanning the budget.

Bricks came into the picture at this stage—1,400 of them from well-used pavements. We decided, as we looked at the house front, that one clearly defined horizontal line was there already, formed by two low, wide, stone steps that led from the middle of the terrace to the lawn. By leaving them as they were, but replacing the stone flags of the terrace with brick, we should gain a second horizontal line of a different colour, thus breaking the height of the house which had been accentuated by stone steps, stone terrace and stone walls, all of one colour. Our third horizontal line was formed by new terrace rails, painted white. The fourth line we are achieving, as silver-lace vines, *Polygonum auberti,* wind their way along a three-barred trellis that stretches across the front of the house between the first- and second-story windows. It is astonishing what those four lines of contrasting colour have done, grey of stone, red of brick, white of rails, green of fast-growing vines. Between them, they've knocked off ten feet of unwanted elevation already.

With the little wing, just the reverse was called for. Vertical lines were needed to lift the ridge of the roof. Here the solution was easy and familiar—a three-foot cupola, topped by our three-foot weathercock from the Tyrol. The combination seems a happy one, but we're sorry we did not think of it while the wing was going up. Hindsight costs a good deal.

Bricks attended to, I found time to set out a few primroses and one large English lavender bush, the latter rein-
forcing the herb bed under the kitchen window. My share
of the day's work seemed too little, my wife's too much,
for she finished rotary-ploughing the rest of the garden.
She certainly has tamed that machine of hers. It comes to
heel as docilely as we wish Garry would.

What a rascal he is! I never knew such a one for his
own comforts and his own way—except, of course, his old
pal Eugene. He *could* be finicky. Nothing could sway him
from the usual order. Getting his drinking water as he
liked it was an example.

"Thees vatter eet iss not boil. Vatter from spring eet
mus' be boil. I not drink eet without boil!"

Garry cares not a fig for that, but he does like his order,
too. Every night when things have settled down and the
library fire glows softly, he stretches out full-length on the
rug to sleep. Preliminary sighing would put Lady Macbeth
on her metal. Then come the snores. Such snores! Later on,
outside at 2:00 A. M., well rested, he barks happily at his
own echo across the Valley, whenever the moon is full.
We're glad our neighbours are not near.

LAST SNOW was followed by heavy frost, far more
damaging. We did, however, go ahead with our seeding,
putting a row of flowers along the edge of the garden, for
cutting and transplanting later—zinnias, gaillardias, Shasta
daisies, asters, summer chrysanthemums, calliopsis, scabiosa,
snapdragons—simple varieties that grow readily in plenty
of sun and will stand a lot of cutting. Few things have
proved more useful than that row. Or less trouble.

While we were at that end of the garden, my wife dressed
the soil where the strawberries were to go with chlordane,
using two-thirds of an ounce for 72 square feet. When

Horace brought the strawberry plants, we found they were Big Joe, Red Star and Blackmore, 33 of each. The choice was his. They have done well. He also brought with him 2 chestnut saplings to plant above the springhouse. We hope that they will grow. How deeply we miss the great trees that grew everywhere when all the world was young and chestnut clubbing our delight in fall.

THE 4TH OF APRIL it went to 18 degrees—scarcely balmy for young buds, yet the bloodroot and the liverwort, fuzzy as ever, paid the cold no heed. They seemed to like it. A song sparrow got into trouble that same day, flying into the toolhouse but not being able to find his way out again. It took quite a time to cup the little fellow in my hands as he beat against the windowpanes. It is so easy to harm a thing so small and in such terror. Or have him harm himself. I was glad when he flew safely away, released at the barn door. Garry was hopeful in pursuit, but could have saved his breath.

THE BROTHERS from Uwchlan ploughed and harrowed our east field as soon as the cold had ended. Can anything be more cheering than the sheen of a fresh-turned furrow?

I thought of the old days as I watched the ploughshares curling the soil over in long, sleek waves, so surely and so swiftly, just as I had thought of the past while watching our ploughing for wheat last fall.

So much has changed in farming ways. So much is basically the same. Back in 1784, for instance, the Revolutionary War just one year over, there were only eighty-two farms in our township. On these farms, containing 10,000 odd acres regarded as taxable, only 830 acres were sown.

That surely is different from today, and thought-provoking indeed, when we consider that people lived on what they could grow. If a man wanted bread for his family, he usually grew the grain himself or went without.

Farmers raised much the same crops then as now, but we have brought more land under the plough and far more cattle are grazing on the slopes. The old system differed from ours chiefly in the use of clover. They had none. I thought of this as I watched the brown of the furrows gaining, the flattened cowpeas disappearing. What fertilizer they would make! Needless to say, though, we were sorry for the loss.

In the earliest days the standby crops were corn—the Indians gave that and taught our forebears how to use it— wheat, barley, rye and oats, with some buckwheat and some flax. We have little of the last two now. Otherwise, there has not been a very great change in rotation apart from the clover.

It is hard to believe there was none of it in Colonial days when these farmlands were first cleared nor for a hundred years thereafter. Its introduction here came in 1793, to be exact, when clover was first grown in our county at nearby Honeybrook. Clover seed cost $20 a pound, a fearful sum in those days, but it transformed the land. More rye was grown at first than wheat. It fared better on poor soil. Much more barley was raised than now, most of it going to the malthouses in town. A surprising amount of spirits was distilled locally, whole hillsides once being set out in apple and peach orchards, the apples serving for applejack and the peaches for brandy. Far more plum and cherries were to be found on the hills than we see now. They, too, were used for spirits.

One thing is often misunderstood. People drank a good deal in those days, there's no gainsaying that, but the quantity of liquor distilled from their orchards was the result primarily of a lack of roads and of wheeled transportation. Until clover came, the hillsides could not be properly seeded and grazed. They were too steep for constant ploughing. They could, however, support fruit trees and so pay their way as the rest of the land had to do. Hence the early orchards. The fruit of these orchards was a different matter. There was no market at all for it. And no adequate means of transporting so perishable a crop, had there been one. Converted into whiskey or brandy, the products of the hillsides could easily be carried in kegs by horses. Roads and wagons and cattle grazing on clover-sown hills changed this.

As I TURNED from our ploughing and saw the cornfield, I could not help but contrast the 40-inch rows with the old method. Once rows were 6 feet apart, with rye seeded between them. People are beginning to try that system again. It has the advantage, they say, of cutting out cultivation and of keeping down weeds. There is no new thing under the sun, saith the Preacher.

To get plenty of sun, rows were run due north and south whenever possible, regardless of slope or contour. We must have lost a lot of topsoil, thanks to that.

All grain was broadcast by hand. There was no other way of seeding it. It seems hard to believe that not even the scythe was used in grain harvesting till the 1800's. Until then, every blade of wheat and oats, rye and barley was cut by a sickle. We've come a long way, down the years, to tractor and seed-drill, combine and baler.

A SCARLET TANAGER, bright as flame in the hedge, brought an end to my dreaming. High time I was seeing

to the lime that must go on as soon as the oats field had
been harrowed.

We are conscious of colour in the spring and respond
to it happily. Almond and flowering quince gave us full
measure near the terrace. Fallen blossoms of the maples
reddened the ground by the hedgerow where the tanager
had been. Tiny leaves of their own particular green showed
on the larches. Virginia cowslips along the bank by the
spring added their blue to the daffodils' gold.

Looking ahead to things more mundane, we put in some
Alfred and Elderado blackberries above the garden. We
also worked a bit of lime into the soil near our clematis.
It can't stand much acidity.

By now blossoms were everywhere, Loddon lilies, candytuft, cherryblow bewitching us. They must have bewitched
our cardinal as well, for he took to bashing himself against
the windows all day long. Cardinals will do this when they
see their reflections in the glass. It is distressing. Actually,
they are defending the demesne of their nests from fancied
rivals.

ONE OF THE LOVELIEST sights of spring was a
glimpse of five doe standing motionless on the slope near
Fox Hollow, their coats as rich in the sun as that of the
courting fox. Above them fresh green formed a perfect
backdrop. The grace that nature gives cannot be described,
but it can be caught in memory and cherished. I'll not
forget those Fox Hollow deer.

NEXT DAY we seeded 8 acres, using 600 pounds of
5-10-5, 6 pounds of timothy, 14 pounds of alfalfa and 8
pounds of brome-grass, mixed with 1 bushel of oats to the
acre. A good man on a good seed-drill brings beauty to a

field, for soil in tilth is always beautiful. Under soft April skies with a hint of rain, it was more lovely still. We had not known till we began farming here that our county saw the first practical seeder used in the United States. That was just 113 years ago this summer.

IF IT ISN'T the fields, it is the flowers or the vegetable garden that calls us. Seeing how bare the dry-stone wall was below the roses on the bank, we planted the edge of it with more ivy, putting in 54 vines this time. By the steps leading up to the garden lane, we planted 3 virgin's-bower for scent as well as for blossom in the fall. Speaking of blossoms, we were glad to see our dwarf Tartarian cherries in flower. This was their second spring since planting. We had not looked for flowering so soon. To keep the chionodoxa and the grape-hyacinths company, under one of the sycamores, we put in 5 or 6 English daisy plants. They do well here, especially if planted in some shade and given plenty of water.

About the middle of April we began work reclaiming the meadow above the spring. Mention has been made of the number of trees cut down during the summer, most of them by Bill from the Corner, as we call him. While he swung the axe, I helped drag the saplings to the piles for burning. Or I sprayed the poison ivy and honeysuckle that had turned the place into a wilderness. When we got the trees down, my wife joined in with her cutter-bar and chewed through the wild tangle of dead vines until they were ready for raking and burning. The slope has begun to look more like a meadow already. Here and there we have left some good cedars and a walnut or so for shade.

I think that Bill and I averaged, between us, ten trees cut, lopped and piled each day we were at it. Usually Bill came to help three mornings a week. None of the trees we cut were doing any good where they were. Those large enough to be sawed into firewood were not burned in the piles with the rest. Good trees, ash, walnut, poplar and a dogwood or so we spared except where saplings were clearly overcrowding each other.

All this was hard work with little nonsense about it. After all, one cannot make light of tree or axe, for both are dangerous. Trees down and the day's work over, it was pleasant to relax a bit on the terrace, warm and snug now, and have a cup of tea outdoors. For a longer break, my wife and I put up a basket lunch and drove down to the Worthington Valley in Maryland to see Marchized, with Smithwick up, win the Maryland Hunt Cup. What fun it is, year after year, to meet old friends in such a setting, everyone picnicking on the hillsides near the course. Or how disappointing it can prove not to meet them. This year our neighbours from Fox Hollow had arranged to share lunch with us, but both missed the other. That speaks well for the size of the crowd. Better luck next year.

AT HOME watering borders started in April—a necessity we have never faced so early. The long drouth had begun. We also had to water new shrubs very early in April and keep it up—rose-of-Sharon, wychhazel, mockorange and the rest. Soil in the coldframe dried the quickest of all. Seedlings there needed watering every other day. The wildflowers under the lilac clump got their share, but white wakerobins, when they began to open, more than repaid us for that slight labour. Bugleweed, the ajuga, soon reared its blue spires near the trilliums. Foam-flowers came a little later. Tulips were catching up with daffodils and the bleeding hearts. Apple and pear, dogwood and silver-bell were in flower. Best of it all, this year's wild strawberries blossomed on the hill.

We celebrated their return by having our first rhubarb. Summer feeding had helped that enormously. Garry celebrated by gulping down a robin's egg, still warm, that he found in the grass.

Weeds needed no rain. They sprang up as persistently as ever. I must say the oats did the same. It amazed us to watch how green and sturdy they showed on the hill. Wheat took longer to make up its mind, though it had been in the ground since fall. Finally it, too, answered April sun and began to grow.

By the barn the hollyhocks we had transplanted in autumn were full of life. Plenty of manure had helped them. When they blossomed in July, we wondered if children still make hollyhock dolls from them. Probably a few do.

IT IS STRANGE what happens when soil is exposed to fire. On the spot where Frank and Bill had helped burn brush piles two years ago, this year a carpet of wild pennyroyal sprang up. There had been none there before—not that we'd noticed. For over a year nothing whatever had grown there. Then out of the blue—should we say out of the ashes—came masses of pennyroyal, racy with scent when stepped on or crushed in the palms. We have put some of it with the mint by the kitchen window. We owe a lot to the herbs there and to the sweet savour given us so generously when they are touched by the sun. The colour and scent of the lilacs nearby are another guerdon for whatever care has gone to them.

MAY DAY gave us a chance to clear most of the wood ash from the fireplaces and spread it around the roses. Old-fashioned, but it works. Wood ashes on rhubarb are especially useful. I suppose it is the potash that helps. We

kept enough ash on the hearths to carry us over to fall.
That brings luck you know. It also makes it easier to
kindle new fires when the time comes. Luck, though, is
what counts. A cricket indoors made matters doubly sure,
as he chirped away as merrily as you please. What more
could we ask?

Speaking of the hearth brings to mind the great copper
kettle we use there to hold logs. One never stops learning.
Neither my wife nor I had the least notion what it was
originally designed for. We supposed it was used at hog
slaughtering when boiling water is needed in quantity to
cleanse and soften the bristles. Probably that was one of its
uses, but not all. The other day a neighbour, born in these
hills, saw the old kettle and enlightened us further.

"That's an apple-butter boiler," she told us. "Sure as
sure. When I was a little girl, every farm round here had
one. They'd set it up in the yard full to the brim of cider,
then they'd build a fire and let the kettle boil all day,
twenty-four hours maybe, till half the cider had boiled
away. Next day all the farm wife's friends would come
to snip apples. The pieces were tossed in the boiling cider.
No—no sugar. That's the new way. It's not half as good.
Those old-time apples were sweet enough as they were.
When the apples and the cider had been rendered into
apple butter, they'd put it in wooden pails or in the old
crocks they had for keeping. The crocks were sealed with
brown paper soaked in vinegar. I can see them now. We
lived in those days and had a lot of fun while at it!"

I'm sure they did. Right now there is no one in the valley
who can hold a candle to this friend of ours where good
cooking is concerned. Or who is better liked by everyone.
We're always learning something from her—the wise old
ways that have proved their worth. Only the other day
she reminded us that a stable lantern set in the vegetable
patch at night will discourage the ravages of coons and

possums, skunks and groundhogs, especially when corn is ripe.

How observant of the land the old-time people are. Another friend of ours asked us recently if we favoured a planned diet for livestock. Naturally we said that we did.

"Who plans it?" he innocently inquired.

"The County Agent. The State College fellows. Department of Agriculture. There's hundreds of pamphlets. The very latest in grass and all."

"That's what I thought. Ever see cattle balance their own diet? Or horses?"

We hadn't thought of that.

"They do, you know. All animals do. Then along comes man, with his book of directions, and makes a nice green field, not a weed in it. All one colour, too. All one sort of pasture. That proves it's a fine field and he's a fine farmer. Well, doesn't it? Stock takes a look at it, has a bite or two, then, like as not, gets a good dinner down by the hedgerow, if they're lucky, where there's some variety. A nip here and a nibble there and all of it just right for their own insides. They know. Proper diet? We're stuffing the poor things full of one thing all day long because we like the colour of the field. How'd you like to eat spinach three times a day all your life? It's all one colour!"

We did some thinking after that.

Our friend wasn't trying to be funny. He had kept his eyes open during a long life, as most of us do not. Among other things, he had come to know animals first-hand, and understand their needs. You can't get it all from a book.

EARLY IN MAY we had some wild poke for lunch by way of balancing our own ration. Had we been more alert, we could have cut lots of it well before asparagus

came. Properly cooked, poke can be delicious, especially
to country palates. Until this year we had not realized how
much we had of it in the upper hedgerows.

As spring advanced wildflowers, of course, were everywhere. Knowing where to look for them now, we got off to
a better start this year. Neither my wife nor I pretend to
be experts at it or even good amateurs, but we do love wild
things growing in their natural setting. We're trying to
keep our small wildflower corner from becoming "pretty"
or "sweet." We hope it will just stay wild. On the slope
of our hill given over to them, a field we shall not even try
to reclaim, the humblest bloom is welcomed when we find
it—shepherd's-purse, cinquefoil or the tiny blue of the
speedwell mean as much to us as roses.

While we were looking for some hidden moneywort one
day, Garry uncovered a rabbit's nest, warm with the softest
fur. He brought two tiny bunnies to us, unharmed. Later
in the summer, however, when rabbits were larger and
would run from him, I'm sorry to admit that he overtook
some and was not too careful of his handling. One can see
we haven't taught him very good manners for a game dog.

BY THE OLD ROCKS, as crocus and snowdrop and
snowflake passed, clusters of scillas prolonged the spell
with brightest blue, holding their own till roses blossomed
above them. Nearby the wrens had a look at houses for
rent and selected two, one on each of the terrace sycamores.
It wouldn't seem home at all without them somewhere close
at hand. We'd miss the chipping sparrows as much for
they're just as friendly, congregating in the matrimony-
vines on the side of the barn.

More birds than ever were about this spring, probably
because we had no cat. Every day almost we saw a pair of

mourning doves in the lane beyond Pippin Hill. Their nest must have been somewhere low to the ground in the fence line. Kingfishers were constantly over the stream, apparently sharing its patrolling with the bluejays. What a hubbub both birds can raise; one clattering, the other screaming, both unbelievably harsh in their notes. To see a kingfisher leave his perch on the slanting willow and dive for a fish is a sight worth waiting for. He rarely misses. I can see his willow now as I write, but he is not there today. The jays are.

Of all the birds we have here, the barn swallows are the most graceful. They seem to dip and dive, bank and turn, for the fun of it, tireless in flight, hour after hour, as twilight comes on. Actually they are catching insects for supper. Our barn shelters scores of their nests, made of plastered mud, high up by the eaves.

The song we like best in spring is that of the meadow lark, for it more than any other carries us back to all the springs we have known and loved. He always keeps reminding us that spring is here! spring is here! The wood thrush's song is another of our favourites, so cool it can be at evening, like water flowing among rocks.

Warblers are in every tree, it seems, but their very numbers and variation defeat us. We wish that we could spot them during spring migration, but there just isn't time from our other chores that press. There's something wrong about that. We love the warblers in their olive coats. We wish them well, whatever their family may be. A beautiful little chap perched one day on the swaying tip of a Norway spruce and did give us a good look at him—a pine warbler, he was, as far as we could tell. How we envy those who really know birds at sight. So many birds seem fond of the roadbed of our lane. Are they dusting there? Or seeking grit for their craws? They need both.

EARLY IN MAY this year I watched a small red-wing blackbird dive at a crow, down near Merlin. He kept diving until the black-coated curmudgeon fled the field. A few days later by the stream here, I marvelled at two catbirds swooping at a great bluejay till they forced him away from the water and out of sight. Jays are killers in spring, ill-grained and cruel for all their beauty, delighting to destroy every fledgling they can get. It is horrifying to see a young wren reaching innocently for its supper seized by the neck and dragged bodily from a wren house by a jay. The cat-birds, I dare say, were protecting their family when routing the intruder. Kingbirds, like catbirds, have rare courage and use it. Few are the foes they will turn from.

Each year we vow we'll find time somehow to study birds properly; at least get to know a few more of them by sight and note and colour. Each year the flowers, the garden and the crops ensnare us. We love it all, of course, but we owe a bit to the birds. They, too, have lived in Arcady.

*"Thou makest the outgoings of the morning
and evening to rejoice."*

9

HARVEST AHEAD

HOW SHORT A TIME AGO the world was still a
green and pleasant place where quiet reigned. How recent
is the horror we have made of it. Could the mind of man
have pictured, a century back, anything so appalling, so
damnable, as that which has been done to the countryside
in our day? Or what is happening to the roads today? Or
to the rivers?

To drive for an hour on most highways, in the East at
least, is to reach the abyss. Has any culture of the past,
savage or civilized, produced sights more hopeless than
these—the very flower of what we call progress? It breaks
the heart to realize we're still at it. The clutter, the cheap
vulgarity of it all, the tawdry blatancy of mile upon mile
of billboard and shack, oozing like some horrible fester
from city to city, beggar belief. Everyone knows this is so,

yet, and to our shame, we pay scant heed to these things. So numbed have we become to what is hideous that we accept it as commonplace. If anything could justify the annihilation of our civilization, surely the desecration of the natural world we live in would prove us a worthy mark.

It is sad to think that we have done more in fifty years to pollute the loveliness of the world than all the millenniums of mankind before us. There is no more shocking commentary on our barbarism than the fact that we have come to regard as normal the spewing of these sores from one end of the country to the other. We're told that really this is proof of our high standard of living.

It is a sorry thing that May, the green and lovely month, should bring this home to us so bitterly, but it does. Yet May also brings a promise of a hope. Just as winter passes and the new green world, the old world eternally young, comes into its own again as fresh as the first created spring, so in time by the grace of God we may find again and value the beauty we have spurned. Here and there we catch hints that are heartening. Many are aware that efforts are being made to curtail prostitution of the great arterial roads. Nature works with patience. Give her time and she will heal even the scars we are so proud of.

HERE IN OUR GREEN CORNER of the hills, May is kind past telling, bringing loveliness and healing to field and woodland. Work soon falls into the natural rhythms of spring. There's time for it now, the long light giving one a chance to finish things without the earlier pressure. First off, came seeding. We put in a good deal of sweet alyssum and annual candytuft this year between the clumps of iberis blossoming outside the terrace ha-ha, thus carrying bloom there from May till frost. Some portulaca, seeded in the edge of the borders, never showed at all. That's the first

time we've missed with anything so easy. Rightly we're
ashamed of it, for we must have been careless. "If your
backcast is poor," we are told in *Memory Hold the Door*,
"your forward cast will be a mess." That is the word for it.

O NE D AY our neighbour Philip brought over a basket
of dogtooth violets—the trout lily—as a surprise, to go
with our wildflowers. The plants were fresh dug beside his
stream, not half an hour out of the ground when we put
them in. These are lovely flowers that go by many names.
Once they were called yellow snowdrops. Some call them
adder's-tongues. To others, they are fawn lilies. The name
makes no matter. It is the kindness that counts, as well as
the beauty of the flower. How anyone could have such good
neighbours as we are blessed with, we don't know. Fact is,
no one could.

O N THE SLOPE, in our rough field there, more wildflowers were opening every day—buttercups, golden
groundsel, wild basil, May-apples, dewberry, blackberry,
stars-of-Bethlehem, Jack-in-the-pulpits, big and small kind,
watercress where the spring overflows and sweet-haw by
the wood. They used to call the May-apple wild lemon. The
fruit is edible, but leaves and roots are deadly poison.

I N OUR BORDERS by the terrace, the azaleas and
pinxterflower—the Swedes along the Delaware named it
so for Whitsuntide—leucothoë, and peonies and carnations
had blossomed. Myrtle, lilies-of-the-valley and bridal wreath
brought colour to the drive. Early in May we transplanted
a good many orange cosmos seedlings from the coldframe
to the borders and set generous clumps of them on either

side of the terrace step just outside the wall. They have blossomed there steadily all summer, holding their own against drought. We never grew cosmos more satisfactory than Orange Flare. White cosmos in the borders and some yellow there were more than dependable. We went astray, however, with a rose-coloured, pinkish sort. It fought too much with other blossoms. How hard it is to think ahead of everything and use what wits we have. At times, there are stumbling blocks a-plenty to cope with.

IN THE VEGETABLE PATCH we ran into trouble with peas. The double rows came up sturdily enough, but did not take kindly to the wire supports we had proffered them, finding it easier to flop over and trail on the ground. With interlaced sticks, they have always clambered up of their own accord. We remedied this year's handicap by running lengths of binder twine along each side of the wire about a foot from the ground, staking the strings just outside the peas. This held the vines in place till their tendrils took hold. As we've said, sticks seem better. Furthermore, they cost nothing and actually require less time to put up than does the wire netting.

All this while, we mulched and mulched till the last shred of Eugene's cuttings had gone on the rows. Faced with so devastating a drouth, I doubt if we could have gathered much from the garden this year to eat, let alone to freeze, without that moisture-saving cover. As weeks of sun grew into months, we soaked each row in turn for hours, watching the water level of the spring. Without mulch all this precious water would have evaporated in a few hours. Soaking down through the mat of dried grass clippings, it reached the topsoil and the roots of vegetables where moisture was needed.

One awful moment came when the spring level suddenly

dropped four inches in a few hours—and kept on dropping. We thought the end had come, till Philip, called in on the run as he always is in emergencies, assured us that the wall of the springhouse must be leaking at foundation level. It had done this before. Nothing to bother over. He'd mend it. In half an hour he had found the weak spot and plugged it with puddled grey clay and grass roots. Before dark the water had risen again and soon was back to normal. We are grateful for such a neighbour and for such a spring. In emergencies Philip surely makes up the hedge for us and stands in the gap, as they used to say.

Later in the summer, fearful of the improvised plug giving way some wild winter's day, we took steps to have the foundations of the springhouse made watertight—a muddy job, but not too difficult.

GOLDFINCHES, great flocks of them, were with us now, just as they had been a year ago, dipping up and down in flight, as neighbourly as ever. What a pleasant tinkling note they have. Each morning at sunrise—we get up early— I could see a brace of wild duck on the water across the lane. Their clutch had produced a family of wild ducklings now. It was a delight to watch the widening arrow of the wake each one made swimming in that quiet pool. We hope the snappers didn't get them.

DAYDREAMING HAS ITS PLACE and what for no? But it doesn't go too well with things that are sharp of edge and fast of motion. One mid-May morning too cool and clear and lovely to be believed, I set to work cutting close in among the flowers that top the ha-ha where the wall ends and the lawn begins. I was using, for the first time, that handy contrivance, a tiny, powered, rotary-blade trimmer, just four inches wide. I could poke it anywhere and draw it back as easily. That was just the trouble. I drew it back too easily—smack against the inside of my near foot. I do not suppose it stayed there the flick of an eye, but the tiny blade was sharp and moving fast. A heavy farm boot meant nothing. No great damage was done, but I found myself in the hospital being sewed up and shot for tetanus before I knew what had happened. That was another lesson learned—at some cost.

The day was redeemed in part for that misadventure by the blossoming of the first Colonial rose—Old Scotch. A fortnight later, Marie Tudor, Old Moss, Rosa Mundi and Damascus had joined it. We knew then that the Colonial bed was a success.

WE MISSED EUGENE and his scythe this spring, for he had saved so much more dried grass than we had realized at the time. We tried our best to follow his example, but our piles seem pitifully scant compared to his. Of course, we have had far less grass to start with and less hay to mow. The drought saw to that. One thing did help our store of next year's mulch. In mowing and baling hay in the lower west field where our small orchard is, we baled no grass at all from the area of the trees, fearful that some spray from them might have reached the alfalfa and timothy beneath. It is impossible to be too careful of this. No one will take chances who has seen three fine Jersey heifers die in bloated agony, just because they had reached over a fence and got at grass contaminated by spray from a neighbour's tree. I saw this happen as a young man and have never forgotten the suffering involved, quite apart from the loss of stock. The hay cut among our saplings here was not wasted, of course. We raked it all and carted it away for mulching. The spray, if there was any on the grass, can do no possible harm to vegetables a year from now.

All this time, since the day we moved here, our goal has been grass. We've harped on that before, but it is the key to everything. At the start we felt a field a year was the best we could do, so heavy was the initial cost of reclaiming the land. Yet so far we have been fortunate past dreams, for by this spring and early summer we have four fields in grass, just doubling our hopes. This week we have ploughed our last three fields for winter wheat and permanent sod next spring. The drought has broken and soil turns nicely to the shares.

At the start every field seemed hopeless. Eroded soil, burdock and ragweed had taken over what was left of the land. We ourselves haven't really done much. Even the sound farming of our friends from Uwchlan has not brought about the transformation entirely, though we owe them much. Nature is the ultimate healer, given a chance. We try to remember that. It is hard to express the gratitude we feel as grass comes again to the slopes. We're grateful— proud, in fact, of the new meadow in the making, where scrub and poison ivy and honeysuckle rioted unchecked, shoulder high, a short month ago. That field is not green yet by any means. It's just been burned over. A broadcasting of rye, some autumn rains, and the native blue grass will show in good time. We're confident of that. But we're casting ahead. It's still May with bishop's cap opening in the wildflower patch and the baked ground crying for water. Also, birdsong everywhere as we've never heard it before—to reconcile us a little to the drought.

BARN SWALLOWS are bits of magic in air, as we've said, but chimney swifts seem faster still. We love to watch them coast and fly, coast and fly, as they do in flight. This

May there were many about, but we never tire of their cheerful notes, not beautiful, as birdsongs go, yet surely merry. There is a fascination hard to resist in watching these racers of the sky as they weave and quarter overhead.

LATE IN THE MONTH, I met our wild duck family beside the lane—mother and three ducklings, walking single file to the pool below the mill and in no hurry at all to get there. I thought the duck would surely rise, but she did not, although I got within ten feet of her. Making no sound but moving a trifle faster, all four slid down the bank, like otters coasting. Once in the water, they must have dived, for I lost trace of them. Purposely I didn't wait, for it seemed needless to alarm them. How close the wild comes to us here at Melbrook if we give it a chance.

The scaup and the ducklings were just one more touch with the green world we love, greener now that grass had grown a bit and trees were in fuller leaf, yet with more colour, too, for daisies were in blossom and yellow rocket and clover everywhere, with Solomon's-seal by the big rock, and orange-tawny king-devil and the tiny flowered blue-eyed grass, so easily missed in an uncut field, so quick to fade if picked. Yellow avens would come a little later. Aaron's-rod was not in flower, but its woolly leaves betrayed it. The Greeks used these leaves for candlewicks. Our own immediate ancestors claimed that mullein tea was good for lung trouble.

ALL NATURE DOES NOT LIE out of doors, as Garry discovered one night late in May when a wild commotion in the chimney suddenly caught him off guard in the midst of his snores. Swifts must have been prospecting there for a nest site, and the noise of their wings set him frantic. It was futile to get anywhere near them, but he tried. When Garry really tries, everyone makes way. It seems wiser. The brass hearth screen went over first, as he took it in his stride. An iron kettle that had served for many a year on a hearth in Roscommon went next, knocked off its trivet. Then came the logs, so nicely stacked for next fall's burning. After that, ashes mercifully veiled the havoc —our good-luck ashes, at that. The swifts paid no heed to all this. The flutter of their wings just came and went. Poor Garry, though he peered up the flue, seemed convinced that digging might solve the enigma. We never knew he had terrier blood, but dig he can. It took a week to get the ashes out of his hide, let alone off the bookshelves and chairs. Now, months later—the swifts, by the way, never did build in the chimney—Garry is not too sure. Once or twice a week, just to play safe, he goes warily to the hearth and cocks an ear to listen. The sound of those fluttering wings has him puzzled still.

Garry had plenty of blossoms to sniff by now. Everything seemed to come at once, but that is May. I think we wait for our few simple columbines as eagerly as for anything else, so appealing they can be in form and colour. To offset the wonder, the surprise, that never pall, a hoard of inchworms, more devastating than Pharaoh's locusts, descended upon us this year, the like of which we'd never seen. In places whole hillsides were denuded of leaves in no time at all.

People had noticed an unusual number of small butterflies or moths quite late in fall, but few suspected that we'd have trouble by spring. We certainly had. These autumn butterflies must have been part of the life cycle of the inchworm. Nature, however, is not easily thrown out of step. After a while, the inchworm disappeared and new leaves showed on most of the trees. I must admit it was a relief to stop picking green hitchhikers from down the back of our necks, but here and there lasting damage was done. A lovely elm, some miles away, was twice stripped completely bare. Since then, it has shown no foliage at all and seems to be dying.

RIGHT NOW, although we know nothing about it, we're trying to predict what sort of a winter we'll have by seeing how thick the husks of the corn are. This is a tough one, far trickier than moths in fall. We'll have to consult Horace about it. Probably he favours woolly caterpillars and pays no heed to husks. One thing we are sure of. A really severe winter helps to check the spread of pests in spring, for cold unquestionably kills many of the dormant grubs and egg masses.

IN SPITE OF THE DROUGHT, we had our first strawberries on the 29th, but the first row of our sweet corn had to be replanted. The kernels just wouldn't germinate in soil so dry. It was then that we began our daily watering—five hours to a row with the soaker hose. As a result of this, the second and third corn rows did well. Now in early fall my hard-working wife has been freezing as many as 150 ears in a day. We had no thought of this in May, when prospects of any corn at all were dim.

Strangely the brook across the lane did not show much shrinkage. Bullfrogs boomed from the mill dam as deep-throatedly as ever. Our lawn, of course, soon burned a hopeless brown, then ceased to grow, yet fireflies, when they came, were as plentiful as ever. Where do they live when there is no grass?

How strangely grass can behave. By mid-August every pasture in the countryside was bare, hard-baked and hope-

less. Cattle were feeding on next winter's fodder. Field corn
had stopped growing entirely. Then drought broke, having
shot its bolt at last. Over six inches of rain fell before the
month was out, more than in all the year till then. Within
forty-eight hours of the first rain, the lawn here was as
green as it had been in early spring. Parched fields were
suddenly carpeted so that herds could graze on them again.
Here at Melbrook, our alfalfa took on new life. It even
gave some promise of a second cutting which had seemed
hopeless till then.

None of this was predictable in June. Whatever we
planted then, we watered, even some wild loosestrife put in
by the pasture's edge where our lawn begins. In the old
days people claimed that this shrubby plant with its golden
flowers prevented oxen from fighting if it were fastened to
their yoke. This has given the flower its strange name. How
such things stick through the years. Watering was all that
we could do—and hope for the showers that didn't come.
We envied the swallows. We could see them skimming the
waters of the brook, breaking the surface in swiftest dipping flight. It seemed such a pleasant way to breakfast, for
they were always at it early. Near them, the spatterdocks
had opened. Once they called them brandy bottles. Masses
of blue forget-me-nots overhung the bank where lobelia, tall
wild sunflowers, touch-me-nots and vervain would come
later. Vervain is simpler's-joy, the sacred herb. Once they
wore it to avert evil. There was no sign of drought by the
brook—a green and cooling spot it was. We loved it. And
were grateful, too. All the while our wheat and the oats,
more than a match for it, kept growing, although the hillside seemed like a rock.

Our terrace flowers took no umbrage at drought so long
as we watered them. Without that most of them would have
died in a week. The beds and borders, all close in to the
terrace, made this easy. Impatiens and the deep blue bou-

vardia blossomed the first week in June. The climbing Peach Glow on the library trellis gave us a hint of how extraordinarily lovely it can be in colour. We hope great things of this rose when it's had a chance to root and grow. Carpet-of-Gold was a fortunate choice for the driveway bank, blossoming well for the first year. Max Graf, not spectacular, we liked as much, so compact they were— exactly what we needed and where we needed them. White and yellow iris defied the drought, whether we watered them or not. There's something fetching about white iris, so obligingly it goes with anything.

It's easy to be stupid. With constant watering from April on, we got to lugging the hose wherever we needed it without paying heed to the loops that trailed behind. One day we overlooked the little Washington thorn at the corner of the terrace as we pulled the hose around it towards the old-fashioned roses. Naturally a metal coupling had to reach the stem of the thorn sooner or later. When it did, we just yanked the harder without looking back. That folly barked the slender sapling halfway round and woefully deep. Easily the cut could have killed the tree. First aid with paint and taping seems to have saved it.

TROUBLE KEEPS US on our mettle—that much can be said for it. No sooner were we really proud of our first hay—the alfalfa-timothy, brome-grass mixture we have talked so much about—than the spittle-bug fell upon the alfalfa, a plague that can be as bad as inchworms on the trees. To spray or not to spray, that was the question. We asked everyone. Spray, said some. Don't, said others. Uwchlan voted nay, on the grounds that it was too dry to risk it. We took their advice. It has proved sound. Another year, under different conditions, it might be wiser to spray. We'll wait and see.

THOUGHT OF UWCHLAN always reminds us of an incident so heartless, it is hard to believe that it really happened. But it did. During the Revolutionary War, after the defeat at Brandywine when Washington's army fell back across the Valley towards Warwick, carts filled with wounded bumped their agonizing way along the same lanes we ride so peacefully today. Some of the wounded reached the Friends Meetinghouse at Uwchlan. They were soaked with the storm that had just put a stop to an engagement on the hills to the south near the White Horse. Some of the men were obviously dying. The surgeons in charge of the wagon train found the meetinghouse locked so they hurriedly sought the caretaker who lived nearby and begged for the key. The man refused to give it on the grounds that his conscience would permit no truck with war. The doctors explained that all they wanted was floor space for men who were dying. Again the scoundrel refused. To their eternal credit the unknown doctors then forced the door and got their men under cover. It is hard to read men's minds. The minutes of the Meeting inform us that the action of the caretaker in withholding the key was not disapproved. What the sense of the Meeting was regarding the medical officers who saved the lives of some of their men we are not told. Nor are we informed on which of Christ's precepts the caretaker's act was justified. It would be interesting to know.

It is little wonder that General Washington himself, after Brandywine, aware of incidents such as this and provoked by what he rightly regarded as obstructions put in his way by conscientious objectors, exclaimed that he must have entered the enemy's country. To the credit of our country, it should be said that most men were willing to defend it. Not every pacifist preferred to see a wounded man die in the rain rather than jeopardize his own selfish soul. The Uwchlan affair was far from typical, we may be proud of

that, but things like it did good in the end, for many, ap-
palled by such heartlessness, joined the colours and were
read out of Meeting for their pains. It takes all kinds to
make up the world.

HOW SUDDENLY a farm can come to life. A few
moments back, as I was picturing in my mind the scene at
Uwchlan, nothing was stirring here at Melbrook. The waters
of the brook reflected the willows without the vestige of a
ripple save when the heron moved his stance to fish. Even
the dragonflies seemed quiet. Water spiders, the skaters,
that coast so smoothly without breaking surface, gave the
only sign of action near the stream. The whole place
drowsed, sunk in midsummer calm. Now, half an hour later,
Bill from the Corner is chopping the last of our lopped
branches. A man from the Eagle is busily nipping off sapling stumps with a power saw at ground level where our
axes did not reach. We should have swung them lower and
so saved a cutting over. Our friend from Uwchlan has just
turned in the lane to start work on the top field where the
deer are seen so often. It will be a busy day. High time I
close desk and join them.

On the 11th of June we finished summer planting the
terrace borders, among other things, finding a chance to tie
up the tulip leaves and bend them over, out of the way, till
they could be cut when they'd faded. Some of the flowers
we used this year were particularly successful, especially an
ageratum called Devon Blue. We have spoken of Popcorn
petunias. We've never found a better sort. The stems are
short and hold the white blossoms neatly upright. Too many
petunias tend to crawl and creep. For marigolds we used the
familiar Sunkissed and Spry. They've blossomed right
along. Poppies, seeded last fall, came into flower by mid-

June, about the same time as Orange Flare cosmos. The
Cabbage Rose, Provence, was the last of the roses to bloom.
We'll never regret putting in that rose bed. It goes well with
the weathered stone of the farmhouse. Sweet peas on the
library wall did not do well. Probably the stones reflected
too much heat. Yet they did give us some blossoms. Low by
the edge of the herbs and trailing over the ha-ha, the moneywort half hid its gold among the leaves. They named it
well, for the flowers are bright as sovereigns from the mint.
Our old standby, Loddon Gold, took over the borders as
peonies faded. There's always something coming on to
cheer us. That's why we love the place so much.

Day by day, wildflowers kept pace with the borders. El-
derberries by the lane side—my mother always spoke of the
wine they made from it; melilot sweet clover, on the hill—
white melilot is used to flavour some of the most famous
cheese, but few think of such a thing when they pass the
lovely clover by; yellow sweet clover—called king's clover
once because it wore a golden crown; daisy-fleabane—still
said to drive away insects; early black-eyed Susans—rank
by rank they came to greet us in the wild field where the
cedars are taking over.

As we waited for haying, the usual garden chores kept
us moving—hoeing, weeding, cultivating, twining up lima
beans, tying up tomato plants, thinning bush beans and
corn, beets and carrots. Clipping and trimming around the
borders and shrubs, were not the least of our chores, but I
think we disliked them most of all. Weeds were fewer this
year, thanks to the drought, but they dug in more deeply
than ever, usually breaking off at ground level when an at-
tempt was made to pull them. That threw more strength
into the roots, so that they sprang up with renewed *élan*.
Yet the lack of rain did lessen their number.

About this time Garry found that the two places in the front terrace where we had taken up flagstones to plant our silver-lace vines made cool nooks for a midday nap, especially after the vines had been watered. To prevent this packing of the soil and crushing of the vines, we put up low wire to screen them. Since then the vines have astonished us, though we knew of their growing speed. Whether or not they'll catch enough sun on the north wall to blossom next summer, we cannot tell. In any event, they are serving their purpose with plenty of leafage where we needed it.

Tiger lilies bloomed about the middle of the month. They don't last long with us, probably because we have not had a chance yet to plant varieties that flower in succession over a longer period. We have been lucky, very lucky indeed, with our phlox. This year first blossoms appeared in early May. Those cut back in spring are coming into second bloom, as lovely as ever. We rely on white phlox and Loddon Gold to carry the borders over July and August, the difficult months. Whatever else we can persuade to bloom there does so against a background of white and gold. Bachelor buttons and calendulas, Persian Carpet zinnias, snapdragons and cosmos, some of the latter off-colour, as we've noted, did well until the rain came and the chrysanthemums took over. We stood the pink cosmos as long as we could, then pulled it out. Why should a few clusters of blossom, though lovely in themselves, rob a border of its beauty? White cosmos and Orange Flare we saved. As with everything, it's harmony that counts.

Walking up the hill with Garry to see how in the drought wheat and oats were throwing head, as we call it here, it was heartening to find both seemed to like it. It's good to pluck a head of ripening wheat and roll it between the palms, as the Disciples did, until the grain is loosened, then bite the kernels free from chaff and chew them. One soon learns from the nutlike flavour and the hardness how ripe the head is. I can remember to this day how my brother and I used to do this a lifetime ago walking the fields.

Usually harvest follows its age-old rhythm of hay, barley, wheat and oats, corn coming later in fall. This year on the farms nearby hay was pathetically sparse, although we were fortunate enough to bale a fair amount of alfalfa. Barley, under weeks of sun, ripened almost as soon as the hay. Then right on the heels of the barley, wheat and oats came both together, golden for harvest. We moved the combine from one field to the other; something that is rarely done.

As Garry and I reached the top of the hill, it didn't take long to see that this would be the case. Wheat and oats were ripening alike and both would come a fortnight early. That meant a purchase of grain sacks and no lost time. Things move fast once harvest is upon us.

We'd planted no corn this year and were glad of it, so fearfully all field corn has suffered under the drought. It has not been a hot summer. Rather the reverse, a very cool one. That, too, retards corn which answers best to warm, hot nights, when one can almost hear the tall stalks growing and the scent of it in tassel carries far. Speaking of corn tassels, three days ago while weeding the strawberry row, my attention was caught by a tapping sound. I knew it must be a woodpecker somewhere, but the tapping was strange. I looked at the poplar trunk, but the sound did not come from there. Then the rhythmic swaying of a tassel of corn two rows over caught my eye. There was a downy busily tapping at the tassel itself; the very tiptop of it. I'd never seen this before.

When Garry and I were on the high field, we could see last year's corn, flattened now for the most part, waiting the plough. While Garry investigated the trace of a wood-chuck, I broke a stalk or two of corn to feel how rotted it was, then, for the first time in years, recalled the cornstalk fiddles we used to make so long ago. I wonder if Bill from the Corner ever saw one. They were fun to contrive, by no stretch of the imagination musical, usually refusing to produce so much as a squeak, but we were proud of our craft. That's what counts. What sport it was to make one's play—not stare at something on a screen. Life lived secondhand seems a poor excuse for living at all. We pity those who've missed the cornstalk fiddle days.

Coming downhill, we passed the tufted vetch in flower and Deptford pinks, moth mullein, poke, bladder campion and dogbane. It is easy to dismiss such flowers of the field as weeds. I suppose they are. We must admit that too many don't improve the selling price of hay and most of them spread like billy-be-damned. Let toadflax, the familiar but-ter-and-eggs, get a head start and see what happens. Yet it had its use, a lotion made from it once rating high as a skin lotion, according to country notions. To look at the commonest flower in bloom is to bring home a realization of beauty we had not suspected.

Then, too, these simple blossoms are great tellers of tales, if we will listen to what they have to say, rich with folklore gathered through centuries. This makes them interesting as all good storytellers are. Take poke, for example. A tincture made from its berries used to be a regular specific for rheu-matism. But there's more to it than that. In old time, poke berries properly treated were put in whiskey to produce what was known as Pennsylvania port wine. I wonder if it was not the whiskey-port which cured the rheumatism rather than the lotion. Sounds potent.

Just above the barn, as Garry left to refresh himself with a mudpack near the spring, I knapped off a head of yarrow to enjoy its pungent, aromatic odour. They used to tell us

that it was sure to bring on a nosebleed if held too close.
Why, I never knew. It never had any such effect that we
could see. Also, it is said that tea made from it is a sure
cure for melancholia. We've had no need to test it for that
so far. The old name for yarrow was milfoil, and that is
what the tea is still called. Some medicinal virtue must be
hidden about the plant, people have talked of it so long.
Far back in 1526, *The Grete Herball* refers to yarrow's
healing powers, assuring us that "—it is good to rejoyne and
soudre wounds." So certain were they of its joining powers,
they even called it Carpenter's Grass. Soldering seems a bit
more in the plumber's line than the physician's, but that's a
matter of taste, no doubt. Hardly a flower grows without
such characteristic good or bad. The old names tell.

SPEAKING OF MEDICINAL VALUES, the herbs in
some ways win us most of all, though not for that reason.
Each herb once rated high in the pharmacopoeia, but it is
their scents we like best, they vary so. English lavender is
delicate like its blossoms. One has to feel for it, as it were.
Thyme waits for the sun before it gives off much aroma.
Verbena is more assertive. Basil must be nipped. Spearmint
tells us where it is in any weather. There is no shyness
there. We use it probably more than all the rest, yet it can
be on the churlish side when it starts to spread, liking to
shoulder out everything else. Rue manages to hold its own,
but mint soon smothers our rosemary and leaves the tarragon and sweet marjoram hard put to keep their footing.
Chervil depends on its own reseeding for survival. It never
gives us much scent, good as it is in cooking and salads.

AS THE DANGERS of the drought increased, we mulched
the terrace borders with two inches of peat. This served

to keep moisture where we needed it after the ground had
been soaked with the hose. The ha-ha wall was gay now
and the borders below it, as well as the nearby beds.
Heartsease, pansies, violas, sweet peas, begonias, ageratum,
bouvardia, geraniums, columbines, Jupiter's-beard, cosmos,
heliotrope, creeping-Jenny, Iceland poppies, candytuft,
sweet alyssum, calendulas, cornflowers, phlox, coreopsis,
astilbe, lilies, hollyhocks, petunias, English daisies, marigolds, lemon lilies and all the roses—we have mentioned
these before, but this June was the first time our terrace
really had a chance. One thing we did succeed in—that was
keeping things low in the ha-ha borders, in proportion to
the little wall above them. The wall itself, built without mor-
tar or pointing, has served its purpose as a root-hold for
stonecrop. Too much at times, for we have had to thin out
Sedum acre by the fistful. Its old name was gold moss. What
a waterfall it can make down a wall. And how it likes to
take over the border below if not watched. Hen-and-
chickens spread a good deal, too, in their own slow way, but
from the original root, never taking over what doesn't be-
long to them.

FOR VARIETY, we had a Midsummer's Eve Fire this
year that put all previous ones to shame. I was burning a
brush pile on the hill where the farm lane runs close to our
wheat, when some dried and sun-parched weeds near the
brush broke into flames. It seemed easy enough to stamp
them out. It was easy. Only by the time I had done so,
more weeds and grass had caught fire the other side of the
pile. Nothing in the least exciting—just a foot or so that
needed attention. Before I'd lighted the brush, I had—or
thought I had, which is not quite the same thing—raked
a ring of bare ground around it. Plenty of green seemed a

safeguard. Only last year's dead grass lay like a tinder mat hidden beneath this year's growth. I hadn't noticed that.

It was a bother to choke my way through the smoke to the far side to stamp out the new flames, just little tongues of fire licking innocently here and there. A whack with the rake teeth put an end to them; only there seemed, all of a sudden, to be such a lot to whack at or stamp on. The brush pile, itself burning fiercely, was soon ringed with low, spreading fire. Wisely I gave up stamping and ran downhill for the extinguisher—an Indian tank. That was the first lesson I learned. I should have taken it up on my back in the first place. Luckily I knew just where it was. Filling the tank took but a moment, for the outside tap was handy. Then I disengaged the hand pump and worked it back and forth to build up pressure. The amount of smoke on the hill was disturbing. Not a drop of water came out of the nozzle. The leather plunger had dried and stiffened during the winter. I'd never given a thought to oiling it. Now it was too late, so I struggled up hill again with the heavy container full of water. There was little or no wind. We were fortunate in that. Part of the spreading fire had reached some rocky ground and lost heart. Part was slowing down in moister grass by the hedge. Towards the wheat, however, it was moving fast, eating up grass with appalling speed and a lot more heat to it than I'd counted on. That field of wheat was dry as a bone, and ready ripe for harvest. It would have burned from end to end, I am sure, had the fire reached it. We needed that wheat. And beside it lay the west wood, dry as punk. For a while it was touch and go, but a little water just at the flame's edge will do a lot. Somehow the fire lessened. Between water spilled from the extinguisher's top, the rake and a pair of well-burned boots, I got it out before it could scorch so much as a stalk of grain, but that small fire of brush had burned a lot of grass when we called it a draw.

My wife, away at the time, gave one pitying look at me—
or the sprayer—when she returned, then handed over an
oil-can without comment. In less than a minute the plunger
was working. I must admit my wife's self-restraint was com-
mendable. Her look, however, covered the situation completely. Next time, I'll test the extinguisher before starting
a fire and I'll see that the plunger doesn't dry out, summer
or winter. Also, I'll have the tank handy-by. At least, that's
what I think now.

While it lasted, the blaze produced more fire, more smoke
and more excitement on my part than all our Midsummer
Eves put together. If Puck has a summer haunt on Melbrook Hill, or if he leases our spinney to the Little People,
they must have felt well served, for a fire in their honour,
we are told, is what they crave most on Midsummer's Eve.
They got it this year, full measure! I stank of smoke for a
week. The burned-over patch is not green yet.

THE VEGETABLE GARDEN this season had no Brussels sprouts, but we replaced them with broccoli and eggplant, both of which have done well. It is hard to predict
things. Last year our eggplants fared badly. This year, well
mulched and watered, the plants are making fruit nicely,
bearing immense—what is the ovoid product of an eggplant
called? It seems peculiar that eggplant and potato should
be related, though the blossom betrays it. And odder still
that the nightshade, of which we have plenty, poisonous in
itself, is also akin to the potato. One never can tell.

THE NEW ASPARAGUS BED showed the effect of the
drought before June ended, so we gave it the longest soaking yet, using both sides of the pierced hose in turn: five
hours' spray and five hours' soak. After spraying the aspara-

gus with water, one has to take heed lest the water-laden plumes bend over and break. They easily become topheavy. It is the soaking side of the hose that really reaches the roots. Once we were sure that the ground was wet for several inches down, we mulched heavily with salt-hay. Wind can cause a lot of trouble with asparagus, especially with new plants, for it tends to swing the shoots back and forth until the earth has been pushed away from them at ground level often as far as two or three inches. This lets in air, dries out moisture and raises hob generally. The thing to do is tamp earth solidly about each loosened plant before any mulch at all goes on. Otherwise, the damage is hidden but still at work. A good mulch lends a certain amount of support to the stalks and so prevents excessive weaving back and forth.

WHERE MY WIFE PICKS UP her garden tricks, I don't know. A new one to me was cutting half the roots of a cabbage and tilting the head over when it has reached a proper size, but is not needed yet. This seems to stop further growth, yet it keeps the cabbage head fresh and tender until it is picked.

OUR PLAN HERE is to have one of our coldframes filled with vegetable seedlings in early spring; the other with flower seeds. In due time, both should be transplanted —at least what we need of them. Leftover tomatoes and so on can stay where they are. The same is true of flowers; only this year all I had time to transplant was the cosmos. Masses of Machet mignonette went to waste in the frame. I hated to see this, but the hay and wheat and oats coming so in a rush made it impossible to do everything. Was it Napoleon who said, "Ask for anything—except time?"

IT WAS WORTH waiting a year to catch the scent of that first, fresh-cut hay. Day after mowing, dew-soaked, when the timothy was turned from the swathes with a tedder, the scent was different, yet just as sweet. The third day, cured now and ready for baling, our hay had still a different savour. We love them all.

How can people bear to miss this? I mean those living in the midst of it all, yet blind and deaf to each day's gift.

The breath of our first hay, first token of our goal, seeing Melbrook green again, made us realize as nothing else has done how surely the lines have fallen unto us in pleasant places—which being interpreted, means, I take it, our home pitch has filled the bill.

"For now the Lord hath made room for us."

10

FULL CIRCLE

SOMEWHERE, IN HIS *Valley of Flowers,* I think,
F. S. Smythe tells us, "There is never absolute silence in a
countryside, but peace." That is true. Those who talk of
our quiet really mean they do not hear the sounds with
which they are familiar. A hot day in July when everything
drowses in the noon heat seems still enough until we listen,
as I am listening now.

Upstream a jay is screaming, far off but audible. Somewhere in the briers, a catbird mews faintly, disturbed by
Garry, no doubt. Once or twice, if I hearken, I hear the
notes of a vireo downstream. Which kind I wish I knew.
No heat puts him off note. A song sparrow, not in the least
oppressed by noon, talks softly to himself near the spring.
A crow all of a sudden is warning someone of something,
high over the west wood. A guinea hen must have laid an

egg. Or is she, too, grumbling about the heat? Chippy
barks over by Newington Hill. I can just pick up the sound
of a horse striking stones with his shod hoofs on the Horseshoe Trail where the going is hard. Very far off someone is
hammering a nail in a plank, the sound of the pounding
throbbing like a drum. Nearer by, below the barn, Horace
has begun whetting his scythe. How that sound goes back
through the centuries.

Through all these muted echoes, there reaches the ear, if
heeded, the low, impalpable breathing of deep summer,
faintly caught, a hum, from field and hedge that never quite
ceases, day or night, where life is thriving in the heat as
millions of tiny creatures we do not see or bother over are
going about their lawful occasions. Before listening, I'd
have sworn there wasn't a sound for miles except for the
bluejay and Chippy. It's worth it to tune in now and then,
just to hear what really is going on. One thing is sure—
peace does lie over our countryside, for these sounds are
of a pattern, sweetened by distance.

THE SOUND OF HORACE and his scythe reminded
me how he still envies Eugene's magic with the grass. I
must confess that both men seem nonpareils to me. I batter
down and push grass over with the blade, no matter how
sharp its edge may be. Horace, and Eugene when he was
here, slice the grass, snicker-snack, so surely, so neatly,
close to the ground with no detectable effort.

ONCE AGAIN I am defeated by country skills. We've
mentioned the great brush piles which Bill and I laid up
during the summer. A while back, feeling that they were
dry enough for burning, we decided to have a go at it and
light the largest pyre. Hose was coupled, all we had of it,

extinguisher fetched close by, rakes and brooms laid handy
and we touched the match. Nothing happened. We added a
stack of newspapers, crumpled. That was stupid, for burning paper floats easily, although we stuffed them well into
the pile. A single scrap of it, burning, once on the old
shingles of the barn, would burn us to the ground. The
paper, however, was wasted. It burned; the branches did
not. A gallon of coal oil, then three more gallons before we
were through, did no good. Some leaves flared hopefully;
a few sticks charred. That was all. The great pile, as dry as
wood could be, might well have been made of asbestos.
Three days Bill from the Corner and I tried our best. We
even toyed with fate by leaving the hose coiled and the
Indian tank on its pegs, hoping that laxity might lure the
contrary wood into burning. We risked wind—another
foolish thing—but in vain.

Then, yesterday, Horace laid by his scythe, walked up
to the pile towering far overhead, tramped round it once,
gave it a kick or two and struck one match. This morning
a mound of grey ash is all that is left with a few small butt
ends of saplings that will burn in a jiffy, once I have pushed
them into the core of ashes, still glowing. How did he do it?
One match!

WE'RE ALWAYS HUMBLED with what we don't
know, and we seem to know so little. One result of my wife's
struggle with the honeysuckle tangle, now burned thanks to
Horace's match, was a plethora of chigger bites. Only they
don't bite; they dig in. Many's the battle I've had with
them while on duty with troops in the field. Remedies,
there, were endless and usually futile. Some were more
painful than the chiggers, such as holding the lighted end
of a cigarette near the bite till the chigger backed out. That
was the theory, at least. If you burn yourself too much, the

chigger—it's always a she, it seems—is said to dig in deeper and lay eggs. You're really in for it then.

A friend of mine, on maneuvers, decided that if only he could consume enough sulphur, his skin would have so unpleasant an odour that not even a chigger could stand him. The reasoning was unusual, but worth a try. Unhappily, the sulphur worked in ways he hadn't foreseen, regardless of what effect it may have had on the chiggers. All day the poor bedevilled major fell out of march to run for the bushes, tearing at his belt. In the hour of need, though, he overlooked the perils of poison ivy on exposed portions of the anatomy, so that the last—or posterior—state of that man was worse than the first by a long shot. Needless to say, the glad word spread. Many a weary foot-slogger was cheered down the last long mile to bivouac by thoughts of havoc at headquarters. Havoc seems too mild for it.

HERE, OUR ELLIE, who knows everything there is to know about a farm, has a far less painful remedy which she swears is efficient, urging my wife to rub the chigger bites with a bit of salt-pork skin, the saltier the better. Chiggers, apparently, have no fondness for salt. Or is it pork? At any rate, the cure seems easy. We'll try it.

How dull life would be without this shift and change of score. We're told we should not despise the day of small things, and indeed we should not or we'll miss half the fun. Horace and his scythe set us on another hunt. Always the commonest things seem hardest to find—a simple, old-fashioned wooden rake it was this time. Metal ones were everywhere, but not wood.

"Oh, you mean those old *wide* ones, all wood? Hay rakes? Haven't had one around for quite a spell. Used to sell a lot of them."

Of course, they're wide. That's what we wanted one for.

And we found it, as we found the wooden stable buckets, by looking deeper in the country.

Coming home that day with the rake, I saw the wild rose blooming across from the spring. It has the same flat, simple flower as the Tudor rose one finds so often on the summer of a door in an Elizabethan house or on the keystone of some country bridge. Near the dogrose, chicory was everywhere. What a cool, true blue it is. And known as far back as memory goes. Horace, not he of the scythe, but the Roman poet who loved the dry Falernian wine two thousand years ago, was fond of chicory at table. The French today make bad coffee worse with it, though they are quick to redeem that error in palate by using some of it in a delectable salad they call La Barbe des Capucins. The French win, hands down, when it comes to names.

ABELIA BLOOMED soon after the wild rose and the chicory. Three names are confusing to the tongue, although we know them well enough: Abelia is, of course, a shrub that flowers in midsummer. Everyone knows it. Lovely hedges can be made of it. We have a bush or two by the front terrace. Iberis is the perennial candytuft. Ours tops the ha-ha wall. And arabis is rockcress. We must get some next spring. The scent of it can be like a breeze from paradise. All three names sound much alike, though it would be hard to find three plants more diverse or used so differently.

AS SUMMER MOVED THROUGH the slower cadence of July, we dusted the terrace roses, but let the bank ones fight it out for themselves. They seem to have made a good job of it, for they're still full of colour.

Hunting for rose dust brought home the need of cleaning the tool shed in the barn, a task set aside for the rainy day that would not come. Why do empty paint cans collect as nothing else does? Clearly they are empty. They'll never be used again, yet row after row seem to gather on the paint shelves. I must have thrown twenty of them away this time, as useless as could be yet carefully cherished. I haven't a doubt but that the shelves will soon be filling again with empties, all in a line and labels to the front, as the old mess sergeant used to muster his tins in the storeroom. Rain or not, we got the tool shed cleaned, even to a hidden store of bent, rusty nails, laid by for emergencies, thanks to Eugene. Some were the century-old, handwrought sort. He must have pried them, one by one, from discarded boards, no easy thing to do.

Eugene could teach us a lot. Among his virtues was a horror of waste, something that most people in our country might take to heart. Nails, as we've mentioned, were especially dear to his heart, but they always seemed to be those of a dream world, all his own, not obtainable here. "Thees iss too thin, Missus! Thees iss too dick! You see? Eet vill not do. Ach! Ach! Nails I mus' haf! Surely there iss nails!"

It seemed a little sad to unearth the old man's hoard, so carefully salvaged and hidden.

COOL DAYS, cool nights and ground like powder did not discourage the birds. Over the west wood a great hawk quartered the sky each day to the displeasure of the crows who scolded, but kept out of his way. Our catbird ran the whole scale of an evening, mimicking first the wood thrush, then the sharp whistle of a cardinal and finally the lower, quavering notes of the bluebirds flying near the martin pole. Garry thoroughly disliked this, staring moodily at the rose-of-Sharon where the bird was enjoying himself. There wasn't a thing the dog could do about it. To make matters

worse, it was his second birthday when the catbird's mockery seemed to reach a peak. Once the various improvisa-
tions had ended, the bird mewed a bit and grumbled like an
old man muttering in his beard. I was glad of that. Maybe
Garry's disapproving stare had reached its mark.

Hummingbirds, though so small, so silent, never fail to
catch Garry's eye. More than once, his inquisitive nose has
been stung by a wasp, giving him the strangest air, part
raffish, part a sort of Disraeli-George Eliot cross, accentuated by his long ears. I think he regards hummingbirds as
overgrown bees—potential enemies—to be snapped at and
gulped or rigidly avoided. He's not likely to gulp a hum-
mingbird. How incredible they are, even to flying backwards. Or is this an illusion? They certainly seem to do so.
Hummingbirds like the tall wild lettuce, using its down to
line their nests.

MORNING-GLORIES were climbing now, bindweed
everywhere in the hedgerows. Worse, there was much of it
rampant in the fields of drought-stunted corn. The white
morning-glory is called lady's-smock in some places, so like
it is to a wide-spreading skirt. We experienced no trouble
from bindweed in our wheat or oats, though that surprised
us for a lot of it had grown there before the fields were
ploughed.

JUST BEFORE HARVEST I moved my old tandem
cart from the kennel loft at the Hunt to our barn here.
During the long years between the wars and after, that cart
had stood there draped in ghostly sheeting. It seems as old
and as odd to look at now as a pharaoh's funerary soul-boat,
but once it was my heart's pride—the very jaguar of youth.

One day, soon after the cart had arrived, I produced what must rank as the prize folly of them all. It could have been more costly than the lawn-trimmer's colliding with my foot. It certainly was just as foolish. Seeing that the heavy brush axe needed sharpening, I got a fine edge on it with wheel and whetstone. Then I hung it on its nails against the tool-shed wall. So far so good. Some imp must have made me more finicky than usual that morning—my wife says I'm finicky all the time—for I decided that the brush axe would be better if hung a foot lower, level with the other axes. As if that made the slightest difference. What limit is there to these crochets? We couldn't credit our own acts if they were performed by others.

Leaving the sharp blade hanging where it was, edge of course curving downward, I proceeded to hammer new nails below it—until, as was inevitable, the curved steel above bounced off its perch and came down like the guillotine on the knuckles of my hand. That's how I know how well I'd honed it. The scar of that nonsense will last quite a while. Maybe I should have bound up the wound with heal-all leaves, the old-time cure? It certainly bled enough. They called heal-all the sicklewort in the old day, which sounds as if others must have cut themselves now and then and found the leaves of it useful.

We never tire of these country panaceas. How or when they started, no one knows. People were familiar with them centuries ago and must have carried them here from across the seas. The virtue of the heal-all is as well known as the little flower itself—*Prunella vulgaris.*

St. John'swort, coming into blossom at harvest, is another plant that can boast its share of folklore. By tradition, the golden flowers open first on St. John Baptist's Day, the 24th of June. I must admit they do come fairly close to it. This is within two days of Midsummer, the longest day of the

year. All sorts of things happen then—witness my fire on
the hill that wouldn't go out. Some things, though, are more
romantic. We're told that St. John'swort plays its part in
casting a young maid's fortune for the coming year as far
as a husband is concerned. Dew gathered from this little
shrubby plant on St. John's Eve safeguards eyesight, so they
say. A bunch of it hung over the cottage door wards off evil
spirits. Some claim it will even stop lightning. How do these
stories begin? One thing is sure—people hold to them.
Many a dried cluster of St. John'swort I've seen by the
doors—just to play it safe.

"You know. The old folks—we've always had it there."

"We think our fathers fools
So wise we grow.
Our wiser sons no doubt
Will think us so."

YESTERDAY, when Garry and I were down by the
brook, we passed some spikes of yellow agrimony. This is
another remedy for the eyes, if the juice of it be made into
salve. That goes back a long way. Chaucer knew all about it.
Every country child once understood that butterflyweed was
called pleurisy root because it served as a palliative for the
ailment. Thoroughwort, its white flowers now marching on
our hill with the first of the woodasters and early goldenrod, is still known hereabouts as boneset because a brew
made from it once rated high in the list of ague cures.

We smile at such tales, yet suppose we check the drugs of
today and see how they, too, derive so often from things that
may grow in our meadows or woodlands. It's like milk in a
bottle—we forget the cow. Prescriptions come from the
apothecary, so we forget how many of them come first from
field or roadside.

GARRY IS THE DELIGHT of our hearts, but we must admit he is not always useful. In truth, he seldom is. One day in mid-July, as I was working in the lane and dreaming of our harvest so soon to come, four cows jolted me from my trance. To be exact, one cow, the matron of those at Pippin Hill, one heifer and two little bull calves, all of them as black and as sleek as good grass and care could make them. Forsaking home pastures, they had breached the fence and now were free-hoofing it down the lane, having a taste of everything eatable on their way. Stolen waters are sweet and bread eaten in secret is pleasant. Only there was nothing secret about this. It seems the easiest thing in the world to shoo a few cows home, especially up a fenced lane—until one tries it.

There are complications. Arley cottage, for one thing. That made an opening to the left. All the black beauties seized the chance to scramble out of the road and scatter happily around the house. As soon as I'd get two of them in the road, the other two would slip past me and start their hide-and-seek all over again. Sound tactics of divide and conquer. I had a rake and used it when in range, but the creatures were so taken with wanderlust that they paid no heed to me. Once past Arley—that took thirty minutes, maybe more—there was the problem of getting the four of them into the Pippin Hill drive. The nearest I've come to that trick has been trying to tilt a lot of mercury pellets into hollow holes. Two in; three in; two out—and begin all over again. As soon as we had crossed the bridge, things eased a bit. At the gate to the pasture, their larking over, all four waited patiently until I had swung the bars; then they walked through as innocently as you please. During my battle with them, Garry remained strictly neutral, mindful probably of the horned apparitions that had appeared on the terrace after midnight when he was a puppy. He certainly lacks the urge of herding in any case.

As I looked at the Black Angus at Kimberton fair, a little later in the summer, their flanks fluffed into prettied curls with flecks of a comb, I could not help thinking of the different fluffs my rake had made on the unperturbed rumps of the cattle in the lane. After all, we're good friends. I didn't thump too hard. Besides, they knew very well that I would not.

ONE SUMMER CHORE that is often easy to overlook is spraying peach trees for borers. We did this twice, using a 50 per cent DDT solution that is allowed to trickle down the trunks of the young trees until the liquid forms a little pool about each tree stem at ground level. In the old days borers had to be searched for and pried out one at a time. Usually the most damaging borer was overlooked. Spraying is more satisfactory and takes little time.

AS EARLY IN SUMMER AS JULY, first hints appear that the year is moving on. A few of the jewelweeds by the spring come into flower. This is the touch-me-not. What a shooter of seeds it can be in fall when the grackles are noisy in caucus and blue lobelias gladden the moist spots. Wychhazel, blooming at the very edge of winter, is another greater shooter. Wisteria likes to pop seed, too, for a surprising distance. Nature has varied devices for carrying on, but certainly few that could equal Garry's coat when it comes to spreading things over the countryside. Every bur marigold for miles around, beggar-tick, stick-tight, whatever you call them, every tick-trefoil, must find a way sooner or later to Garry, especially to his ears. Most of these seeds seem to stay with him until we work some free, but we're sure that hundreds more must be scratched off and dropped along the way. Johnny Appleseed, Garry is, and doesn't know it.

If there is one thing that he loves, as do all springers, it is the water. He met a disappointment at the brook one day that certainly took him by surprise. In repairing a small dam upstream, the sluice gate had to be opened and the water drained. This occurred just at the time the drought finally broke and three glorious days of rain saved the fields and the corn. Naturally, the storm also raised the stream till quite a flood poured through the open sluice, scouring tons of sand from the sides and the bottom of the pool. All this sand came to rest in the deeper reach below the weir, where Garry loved to plunge and where children used to swim. I'll never forget poor Garry's amazement when he first saw the sand in lieu of water. Four feet deep that sand is now, filling the pool from side to side. Not five inches of water glide over it. To make sure what he could not believe, Garry took his customary running jump and landed with startling suddenness and astonishing little splash on what must have seemed to him the top of the water rather than in it. Also, he began to sink in the unaccustomed sand; too shallow for swimming, too soft for treading. No wonder he looked nonplussed, just standing there, amber eyes begging me to tell him what had happened to his pool. And to him. I wish that I knew the answer. Perhaps a new spate will wash the sand bank clear and give us our pool again. Meanwhile, we make the best of it, I on bank, Garry splashing and snorting further down where the willows are, driving kingfishers off perch and sending the heron coasting off with angry squawk. There's life in the old world yet, and Garry seems to find it.

BY THE KITCHEN WINDOW near the herb bed, spicebush berries, green now, will all too soon be ripening to crimson, more to the fore than their inconspicuous yellow blossoms of spring. In Colonial days, when tea was taxed, housewives used the spicebush to brew a substitute. We've never tried it, but it doesn't sound too good. This shrub has always served country folks, however, as a source of all-spice when supplies run short.

IT SEEMS INCREDIBLE that before our harvest was in and long before our vegetable garden had struck its stride, flowers here and there were opening to remind us that the jewelweed was not the only autumn blossom edging into the picture. Nature moves so imperceptibly, so slowly, yet so surely, that we are into one season before we realize that the earlier glory of the year is passing. Tall wild sun-flowers drive this home to us, for they are as characteristic of fall as any flower that blooms, yet a few of them can be found each year at least two months ahead of their time. How immensely tall they are at that, even before they take over the banks of the brook, Brobdingnagian in the height of their stems. The sunflower was a sacred symbol in Mex-ico and Peru when the Conquistadores overran those un-lucky countries. The Indians made plaques of pure gold representing this flower, to wear in honour of their sun-god. How our own Indians, the Lenni-Lenape, regarded it, nobody seems to have noted. Few flowers carry a richer gold so high or with so proud a grace.

Change in colour, everywhere, every day, is endless, once we pause to look at it—or for it. From where I write, a reach of the brook is in view just as the water widens at the bend above the mill. Today, under drifts of northeast rain so fine it is more mist than rain, wind has rippled the water, darkening the surface to jet. On clear mornings, under sun and wind, the brook flows silvery and cool between its banks where the sheep-clipped meadow shows green through the trees. Then again, under clear sun, with no wind, the water is blue, unbelievably deep, like the blues of a Maxfield Parrish mosaic, most lovely but not true. Only these incredible colours are true. I've never seen the stream across from Melbrook twice the same. Even in winter, change is there and always there is beauty—clear ice as green as jade, or snow on ice or snowflakes dropping softly on unfrozen water, each is different. Some might call such colours grey, but surely they are blind who will not see the changes when they come. Despite the falling leaves or winter snow, these colours move us just as the more varied tints of spring, the steady hues of summer and the gorgeous panoplies of fall can stir one to the very soul.

Water has a charm of its own in any weather: quiet reach or stream in spate or deep pool by the willows—dawn mist rising—each brings to us a different mood. Lucky are those who find themselves in tune. So much happens. Life and all its incredible facets seem unending in delight. There is always something new, some fresh challenge. The same is true, of course, of field and hedge and forest. Surely we are fools if we do not drink so rich a boon to the lees. I am sure that people in the old days, when they lived closer to the earth, caught more of the miracle than we do. For one thing, they had more time to see things, which is, in a way, more time to live. The very names they gave to the blossoms about them reveal this. They called the winter aconite New Year's Gift, so early did it come to brighten winter's chill. Love-in-idleness was Shakespeare's name for the pansy. He didn't invent it. He had heard that lovely name and knew that it carried a bit of the green heart of England with it. People looked at the wildflowers once. Thank God, they are beginning to do so again. Once upon a time, they looked at the columbine and called it two-faces-under-a-hat. That's accurate, though not poetic. The point is they knew the flower before they named it.

THE DAY GARRY HAD his contretemps with sand in the stream, I noticed scarlet pimpernel growing by the side of the garden. Not only has it a name that goes a long way back, but it also has a function to perform in the country, for the pimpernel, to those who keep eyes open, is a reliable weather prophet. The tiny petals close on the approach of rain or the threat of it. In all truth, they had a long wait this summer, for not even an overcast day came to us for months. Francis Bacon is said to have been the first to notice the reaction of the little pimpernel to weather. I very much doubt it. Probably he was the first to write down what he saw, but I'm sure a countryman knew all about the flower before the great Elizabethan gave us his account.

ONE STILL FINDS scarecrows now and then standing with outstretched arms in the field of young corn. No doubt they had them in Bacon's time. Why they have persisted so we never could make out. After all, few things in the natural world are more miraculous than the eyesight of a bird. Try walking up to a sentinel crow with a gun or with a stick or barehanded. You will soon discover that the crow knows all about you long before you can see more than his outline. It really seems a bit farfetched to fancy that a pair of old breeches and a coat stuffed with straw standing motionless weeks on end could possibly deceive a crow or any other marauding bird. Someone once said that people keep on making scarecrows because it gives them a wonderful opportunity to express their opinion of their betters. Why not? The Squire usually wore a hard hat. Many a scarecrow still does—or did until the supply of hard hats ran out. What could be more comforting than to see one's special enemy or one's niggardly employer, if that were the case, standing soaked in the winter's rain, a mockery to every crow for miles?

HERE AT MELBROOK as harvest drew near, we were plagued more and more by flocks of pigeons feeding on the oats. They seemed to leave the ripened wheat more or less alone. Crows were in evidence, but never in such numbers as the pigeons. We had no scarecrow, feeling it would do no good. Also we had no enemy on whom we felt an urge to vent our spleen. In the early days, farmers used to hire small boys for a few pennies to keep the young corn free from raiders. Wasn't this the way Jude the Obscure began in Hardy's great novel? We have found that the only thing that has the least effect on crows or pigeons is noise. If a gun be fired, they will circle and disappear, though not for good. In the end we gave up the battle, deciding that harvest was near and there seemed to be a lot of it.

BLACKBIRDS WERE FAR MORE TROUBLE to us than either pigeons or crows. They are canny, thievish fellows, worrying us more than all the rest. From early summer on, they watched the apples near the drive, nibbling a hole in the ripest and sweetest before we could pick them. Actually, this didn't matter too much, for we had more than we could use and were giving away bushels of them among the neighbours. Sweet corn, though, was a different story, especially in a drought year. We had nursed each row along with hours of watering. We had watched the tassels come and then the ears and then the telltale drying of the silk. We had split a few husks to see how the cobs were filling. And then—just as we were ready to pick—often an hour before—the blackbirds would slit the husks and peck at the best of the kernels for themselves. A blackbird's bill is sharp and quick as any dagger. He can open a pea pod with it as easily as corn.

They came quickly, too, when no one was looking, gliding over from the apple tree to the garden, avoiding the first row of corn, which was in view, but settling down to the serious business of supper in the second and third rows out of sight. In the end we scared a few of them off and saved plenty of ears; there seemed to be enough for all, so maybe we shouldn't complain.

One thing did work, but not with the blackbirds—a lighted stable lantern put in the middle of the corn at night. That old trick soon ended groundhog thieving once and for all. Or was it skunks? Garry, though, was thrown on his beam ends by the sight of that light burning there by itself without apparent reason. Even in daylight, before we had a chance to put out the wick, he would not accept it, circling around at a safe distance and barking. Perhaps he connected it with swifts in the chimney, who knows? We wish that he would show half that concern in the woodchucks themselves.

AS ALWAYS HAPPENS if one waits long enough, the drought broke—this time before summer was half over. It rained one night, thank God, and it rained again two days later, a blessed rain, off and on, softly, all day, every drop of it soaking in. And it rained still more a few days after that. One has to live on the land to know just what that meant to us. Surely we were finishing our second year here with the happiest of omens—a fine harvest ahead and now a break in the weather. The day after the rain dawned cool, as it nearly always does, windy and crisp and blue. A day to be alive and we knew it.

Everything seemed full of spice. Dayflowers, bluer than chicory, stayed open on the bank longer than usual before they disintegrated into the strange froth so typical of them. Sparrow hawks, kestrels, they really are, looked more spruce and trim than ever, as if they'd just put on new coats. Few birds so small wear so proudly the air of their lineage. They're falcons, all right, and know it as they hover in the air against the wind. Even the green heron, not much for beauty at the best of times, shitepoke, fly-up-the-creek, we call him, seemed to have felt the wonder of the day as he moved over the water with something of an air. Actually, I suppose he had a fish dinner in mind, not the glories of nature, yet he, too, was a part of the picture. How good it can be just to be alive and see and feel such things.

ONE NIGHT, thankful that the rain had come, we heard a lone hound tonguing on the hills. It was far too early in the summer for any thought of hunting, but the sound of that hound surely did carry me back. When I was a boy, there was much more night hunting than now, in the fall, of course. Indeed, it was the accepted way of entering young hounds to fox. Their cry fell softly on the ear, in those days, softened by distance and the magic of the night, yet carrying for miles in the stilled air.

Long ago, I can remember lying in bed at Bellwood trying to unravel the muted notes that would come to me from across the Valley, when hounds were out. Was that Quickstep now? Or was it Dashwood? How hard it was to say. Old Gabe was easy. Once he spoke, those bell notes needed no second peal. Not often did such music come to me in bed. If I knew hounds were out of kennel, I'd be somewhere within hearing, regardless of the hour, sitting on a post-and-rail fence or hurrying down a country bylane to nick in.

Old hands can spot each hound by name, though in the dark and often far off, the moment he speaks to a line. I knew a few hounds whose cry I could sometimes tell—not nearly often enough, but now and then. It was bliss unspeakable when a known voice echoed against the Valley hill and I could mark it.

"That's Pilot for sure!"

"Might be. Might be. Sounds like."

I knew then, from such terse comment, that I had begun to qualify. Sweet it was to raise my voice among the ancients in the gate. Not quite so sweet, though, when my triumph was nipped by a curt:

" 'Tain't. 'Tain't."

Now, at Melbrook, when we hear hounds chiding at night, we don't know one from another, yet a part of the old-time thrill is there. We know that some fox is afoot under the sickle of the moon. Some hound has owned the line and found it true. That's music enough. But back through the years I've never forgotten the hounds I once knew by name and note—Flirt and Warrior, Chimes and Glancer and Showboy, Ranter and Rocket and Larkspur—I can hear them now. How grateful we should be for such memories. They add the sweet to life as the years glide on.

EVEN IN MIDSUMMER, when there is plenty of browse about, people now and then view the wild deer in the open. A fine buck is often seen in and about Melbrook. Every time someone spies him, he grows in size and splendour. No doubt he is the same buck that Alena and Eugene viewed on the hill here two years ago. I have not seen him myself, worse luck, but I do know that soon his reputation will put Paul Bunyan's ox to shame, such tales we hear of the spread of his horns. They must be like the limbs of an oak by now. Or is that the result of twice-told tales? We'll have to wait and see. In any event, we're proud as can be that Melbrook is one of his favourite harbours. Next winter when he and his family get at our saplings and dwarf trees, we'll not be so admiring. Now, in summer, they do no harm.

THE DEER, HOWEVER, MUST WAIT. Things were moving fast on the farm. When it comes to harvest, there can be no tarrying. One always forgets something. At the last moment, I realized that I had neglected to pick up our wheat permit which we must have before we combined and took grain to the mill. The permit in hand, sacks had to be checked and sorted. It rained a little the night before St. Swithun's Day, not enough to do much good, but the wind did great harm. One or two poplar limbs, twenty feet long, crashed down in the road. They had to be dragged clear, but burning them was postponed. One thing is sure. The best-laid plans are usually changed, but nothing can stand in the way of the fields when they are ready. What we feared most were windrows of lodged wheat and flattened oats to greet us, the morning after the great wind, but not a blade was down. Woe worth the day had there been heavy rain with that wind, for then topheavy grain would surely have suffered and all our year's labour been in vain. We needed rain as never before, but not during that particular week.

On the 19th of July, we began with the wheat, the two good farmers from Uwchlan, reinforced by a young neigh- bour of theirs named Jack and a man to help with the loading, made short work of it. Oats took considerably longer, as there was much more of it, yet we managed to get the last bag under cover by nightfall. We'd waited a long time, my wife and I, to see grain sacks once more in the barn, piled on the old threshing floor. We'd taken most of the grain to the mill already, but forty or fifty sacks were left by dark, so we got them indoors until tomorrow. Had we reaped hundreds of acres, we could not have been more proud.

Three days later we raked our straw, gratified at the amount we got of it, especially of oats. Naturally, we wished there had been more of the wheat for its straw is the best. I wonder if country people still use the straw of rye to weave baskets with, as once they did. No such craft is found near here, but the old baskets were lovely things. Rye straw was also used, when I was a boy, in pressing cider at the mills on Valley Creek. Eheu! Eheu! Those days are gone.

Next morning the harvesters returned to bale. Weather still proved kind. When we had taken the oats straw to the mill, we carried most of the wheat straw over to Jamie's by Pigeon Run and heaved the heavy bales up to the loft for him. Just what would happen to our timothy and alfalfa and brome, now that their cover crops were off and the sun still blazed, we didn't know. Alfalfa was there all right, showing quite nicely in the parched stubble. We were not so sure of the timothy. Real rain, a fortnight later, however, turned the discouraged slopes to green and then to growing. A miracle? We are assured that the showers of blessing will come. They did—in time.

By early fall we had harvested our second cutting of the first alfalfa and the first cutting of the new fields. Few would have felt that possible last spring. A year ago, the very idea of permanent sod seemed too far off for hope. Riding that last load of straw was a thrill that will not come to us again, but we'll never forget it. First harvest, after all, is the first.

The most surprising part of all this, when we took stock of it—hay, wheat, oats and straw—was that our little harvest had paid. Not much, naturally, but it did pay. Mr. Micawber is right—the sixpence makes the difference. Not only were we out of the red and all expenses covered, but we had some fields in good grass to boot. And all the others on the way. To say that we were satisfied is putting it mildly. We'll never have a harvest home quite like our first—in thrill.

TWO YEARS, ALMOST, my wife and I have been here. The farm is coming full circle, not yet what we dream it may be, of course, but on its way. How unbearable even so delectable a place as a farm would be, how unutterably dull, if everything were achieved at the start, without set-backs and effort, all perfect, not a challenge left. We couldn't face it.

Much work and plenty of sweat, with few days off, have gone to fields and garden, but not one hour begrudged. We can see now what these acres once were when all the Melbrook slope was green, for our own meadows are beginning to show life with the healing of the grass.

We have so much to be grateful for—so many have helped us. So many have encouraged our modest borders with gifts of green things growing. Or guided us in weightier matters of the field. We cannot forget the kindly sun and the rains that came in time, though we doubted that they would, and the cool spring water steady in the drought. And Garry, of course. What would the farm be without him? Hard work? Naturally. Mishaps to vex the heart? Why not? That is life. We've lived it richly here, more challenges ahead.

Who'd want to miss the fun of the fair?

Cultivated Flowers, Wildflowers, Trees, Shrubs and Herbs

THAT HAVE BLOSSOMED

THIS YEAR—1954

AT

MELBROOK

CULTIVATED FLOWERS

Aconite, winter
Ageratum
Anemone, Blanda atrocoerulea
Astilbe
Asters
Baby's-breath
Begonia
Bleeding heart
Bouvardia
Calendula
Calliopsis
Candytuft—annual
Candytuft—hardy, Iberis
Carnations
Centranthus ruber
Chionodoxa, Glory-of-the-snow
Chrysanthemum, autumn
Chrysanthemum, summer
Clematis, Duchess of Edinburgh
Columbine
Cornflower
Cosmos
Crocus, snow
Daisies, English

Daisies, Shasta
Daffodil
Daylily
Gaillardia
Geranium
Grape-hyacinth
Heliotrope
Hollyhock
Hyacinth
Impatiens
Iris, Dutch
Iris, Japanese
Jasmine, winter
Johnny-jump-up, Heartsease
Jonquils
Larkspur
Lily, Madonna
Lily-of-the-valley
Lily, plantain
Lily, tiger
Loddon Gold
Marigold, French
Matrimony-vine
Meadow Saffron
Mignonette
Morning-glory

237

Myrtle, periwinkle
Myrtle, trailing
Pansy
Peony
Petunia
Phlox, Divaricata, wild sweet
  William
Phlox, subulata, mountain-
  pink
Phlox, summer
Poppy, California
Poppy, Iceland
Primrose
Rose, Blaze
Rose, Cabbage—Provence
Rose, Climbing
Rose, Cloth of Gold
Rose, Damascus
Rose, Dream Girl
Rose, Floribunda
Rose, Harrison's Yellow
Rose, Inspiration
Rose, Marie Tudor
Rose, Max Graf
Rose, Multiflora

Rose, Mundi
Rose, Old Moss
Rose, Peach Glow
Rose, Repens alba
Rose, Rugosa Spinossissima
  alba
Rose, Scotch
Scilla
Sedum acre
Sedum sieboldii
Silver-lace vine
Snapdragon
Snowdrop, February Fair
  Maids
Snowflakes, Loddon lilies,
  Leucojum
Spiderflower
Sweet alyssum
Sweet peas
Tulip
Viola
Violet
Yucca
Zinnia

WILDFLOWERS

Anemone, rue
Aster, blue
Aster, starved
Aster, wood
Avens, yellow
Basil, wild
Beard-tongue
Bedstraw, rough

Bishop's-cap
Black-eyed Susan
Bloodroot
Blue-eyed grass
Buckwheat, false
Bugleweed, ajuga
Butter-and-eggs
Buttercup

Butterflyweed

Campion

Carrot, wild, Queen Anne's lace

Celandine, greater

Chervil, rough

Chickweed, mouse-eared

Chicory

Cinquefoil

Clover, alsike

Clover, melilot, white sweet

Clover, melilot, yellow sweet

Clover, red

Cowslip, Virginia, Mertensia

Daisy

Daisy-fleabane

Daisy, Michaelmas

Dandelion

Dayflower

Dock

Dogbane, spreading

Eyebright

Foam-flower

Forget-me-not

Globeflower

Golden groundsel

Goldenrod

Hog-peanut

Horse-nettle

Ironweed

Ivy, ground

Jack-in-the-pulpit

Jack-in-the-pulpit, greater

Jewelweed, Touch-me-not

Joe-pie weed

King-devil

Knotweed

Lettuce, tall wild

Lily-of-the-valley, wild

Liverwort

Lobelia, blue

Loosestrife

Lungwort

May-apple

Milkweed

Mint, horse

Mint, wild

Moneywort

Morning-glory, wild

Mullein, great

Mullein, moth

Mustard, wild

Nightshade, woody

Pennyroyal, wild

Pimpernel, scarlet

Plantain, lamb's-tongue

Plantain, ribwort

Pokeweed

Primrose, false evening

Quaker-lady

Rocket, sweet

Rocket, yellow

Rue, tall meadow

St. John'swort

Self-heal. Heal-all

Shepherd's-purse

Solomon's-seal

Solomon's-seal, false

Sorrel

Spatterdock

Speedwell
Spring-beauty
Star-of-Bethlehem
Strawberry, wild
Sundrop
Sunflower, tall wild
Tear-thumb, arrow-leaved
Thistle, bull
Thistle, Canada
Thoroughwort, Boneset

Tick-trefoil
Valerian
Vervain, Wild hyssop
Vetch, tufted
Violet, blue
Violet, white
Violet, wood
Virginia creeper
Wakerobin, white, trillium
Yarrow

SHRUBS

Abelia
Alder
Almond, flowering
Azalea, nudiflorum, pinxter-
   bloom
Azalea, schlippenbachi
Azalea, wild
Blackberry
Bridalwreath
Coralberry
Dewberry
Forsythia
Holly, Chinese

Holly, Japanese
Jetbead
Laurel, mountain
Leucothoë
Lilac
Mockorange
Quince, flowering
Raspberry
Rose-of-Sharon
Rose, wild, Dogrose
Spicebush
Sweetshrub

TREES

Apple
Cherry, Tartarian
Cherry, wild
Dogwood, wild
Dogwood, Kousa
Franklin tree, Gordonia

Pear
Silver-bell
Sweet-haw
Tulip-poplar
Wychhazel

HERBS

Basil, sweet
Chervil
Chives
Lavender, English
Lemon verbena
Marjorum, sweet
Pennyroyal, European

Rosemary
Rue
Spearmint
Tarragon
Thyme, English
Thyme, golden
Watercress